BIBLE CROSS~ WORD PUZZLES

MARVIN KANANEN

HALO PRESS

The King James Version of the Bible has been used
to prepare almost all of the puzzle clues.

References marked LB refer to the Living Bible; those marked NIV refer to the New
International Version; those marked ASV refer to the American Standard Version.

The thirty-five puzzles in this book are purposely designed to help readers uncover Bible truths as they solve the puzzle clues. Approximately 75 percent of the clues are based on Scripture references. Solutions are placed at the back of the book.

Happy puzzling!

1

Across

1. Balaam's donkey.
4. _____ of Solomon.
8. _____ city is like unto this great city? (Rev. 18:18)
12. So they _____ both together. (John 20:4)
13. Greek porch.
14. Woe to them that are at _____ in Zion. (Amos 6:1)
15. Jether's son.
16. Outer portion of the earth.
17. Deliver us from _____ . (Matt. 6:13)
18. Wise men.
20. As a hen gathereth her _____ under her wings. (Matt. 23:37)
22. Quiet!
24. Spanish article (plural).
25. Bartholomew's other name.
30. Give us this _____ our daily bread. (Matt. 6:11)
33. When ye pray, _____ not vain repetitions. (Matt. 6:7)
34. Son of Shema.
35. Lyrical poem of praise.
36. Woman's nickname.
37. Sons of Thunder.
39. Possible nickname for one of Jesus' disciples.
40. Let us _____ good unto all men.
41. Surname of Judas.
46. First garden.
50. Goliath's height: six cubits and a _____ .
51. Crowning work of God's creation.
53. Tokyo's former name.
54. Matthew's other name.
55. Westernmost U.S. city.
56. Upward (comb. form).
57. Two hundred _____ and twenty rams (gift to Esau). (Gen. 32:14)

58. His tail _____ the third part of the stars. (Rev. 12:4)
59. Jacob's fifth son.

Down

1. Son of Shem.
2. Abram's spouse.
3. Unforeseen obstacle.
4. Draft system.
5. Affected with (comb. form).
6. Ark builder.
7. Thou art a _____ . (Mark 14:70)
8. Seventy _____ are determined. (Dan. 9:24)
9. If I _____ walked with vanity. (Job 31:5)
10. There is _____ [2 words] not unto death. (1 John 5:16)
11. Telephones (informal).
19. Hebrew for "Adam."
21. What Jesus did to the sea.
23. Phoenix was a good _____ . (Acts 27:12, LB)
25. Father of Joshua.
26. Third king of Judah.
27. _____ virgins. (Matt. 25:1)
28. The name of his wife _____ , _____ the names of his two sons. (Ruth 1:2)
29. _____ , I am warm, I have seen the fire. (Isa. 44:16)
30. For a living _____ is better than a dead lion. (Eccles. 9:4)
31. Summer refreshment.
32. Yea or Aye.
38. The loving hind and pleasant _____ . (Prov. 5:19)
39. Zoan.
41. There was an _____ that is called Patmos. (Rev. 1:9)
42. I will _____ thee out of my mouth. (Rev. 3:16)

43. Burial place of Jesus.
44. An _____ of sweet smell. (Phil. 4:18)
45. But the tongue can no man _____ . (James 3:8)

47. Salt sea.
48. Ferber or Millay.
49. Hour of Christ's death.
52. To confine in a cage.

2

Across

1. Jezebel's spouse.
5. Wildebeest.
8. Zeus' wife and sister.
12. Miami's county.
13. Electrically charged particle.
14. Prophet from Tekoa.
15. Landed lightly.
16. Cupbearer to King Artaxerxes.
18. Where _____ [plural] and rust doth corrupt. (Matt. 6:19)
20. Lay not thine hand upon the _____ . (Gen. 22:12)
21. The fire shall _____ every man's work. (1 Cor. 3:13)
22. Ignited.
24. Agra's mausoleum.
26. The Hebrew name for _____ is Bereshith.
30. Saul's elder daughter.
34. Esau's spouse.
35. Hawaiian dish.
37. They which are accounted to _____ over the Gentiles. (Mark 10:42)
38. Plural of "woman."
40. Whose children were Joel and Abijah? (1 Chron. 6:28)
42. The sabbath was made for _____. (Mark 2:27)
44. Moments (slang).
45. Damsel, I _____ unto thee. . . . (Mark 5:41)
48. An extinct bird.
50. The beginning of Nimrod's kingdom.
54. Twentieth Old Testament book.
57. God is _____ . (1 John 4:8)
58. And with many such parables spake he the word unto them, as they were _____ to hear it. (Mark 4:33)
59. Bind them continually upon thine heart, and _____ them about thy neck. (Prov. 6:21)
60. Lamb's nom de plume.
61. Arise, and _____ up thy bed. (Mark 2:9)
62. Headgear.
63. Mix thoroughly.

Down

1. The pride of God's creation.
2. Angelic corona.
3. Mine entrance.
4. City of David.
5. The _____ shall take him by the heel. (Job 18:9)
6. Christmas.
7. Doff one's hat in respect (archaic).
8. Son of Noah.
9. To send forth.
10. Will a lion _____ in the forest? (Amos 3:4)
11. Deathly pale.
17. Dutch cheese.
19. Bro's sibling.
23. That he may dip the _____ of his finger in water. (Luke 16:24)
25. The City of Peace.
26. British variant of "God."
27. Former name of Tokyo.
28. Manufacturers' organization.
29. Naval distress signal.
31. For ye tithe mint and _____ . (Luke 11:42)
32. He hath done _____ things well. (Mark 7:37)
33. Egyptian god of pleasure.
36. YHWH, literally.
39. My _____ is Legion. (Mark 5:9)
41. Rabble.

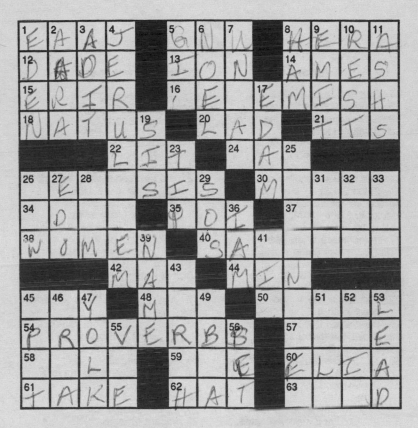

43. And he will stretch out his hand against the _____ , and destroy Assyria. (Zeph. 2:13)
45. He _____ on the ground. (John 9:6)
46. The city of _____ the father of Anak. (Josh. 21:11)
47. Yellow part of an egg.
49. Rehoboam's son.

51. The trunk of a tree.
52. Why, what _____ hath he done? (Mark 15:14)
53. Can the blind _____ the blind? (Luke 6:39)
55. The letter v.
56. A certain man planted a vineyard, and _____ an hedge about it. (Mark 12:1)

7

3

Across

1. God is _____ . (1 John 4:8)
5. Abbreviation for "assistant."
9. _____ greedily after the error of Balaam. (Jude 11)
12. God cannot be tempted with _____ . (James 1:13)
13. A festive occasion.
14. The serpent beguiled _____ . (2 Cor. 11:3)
15. Let us not _____ it, but cast lots for it. (John 19:24)
16. To be in reverence (poetic).
17. In that place where Martha _____ him. (John 11:30)
18. A man hath no _____ above a beast. (Eccles. 3:19)
21. Arthur's lance.
22. This will we do, if God _____ . (Heb. 6:3)
25. Pope when Luther rebelled.
28. A colt, the foal of an _____ . (Matt. 21:5)
30. _____ , thou art the Son of God. (John 1:49)
31. Continental U.S. westernmost point.
33. Final Hebrew letter.
35. A _____ and a pomegranate. (Exod. 39:26)
36. To melt ores.
38. To feel ill.
40. Unit of reluctance.
41. Heaven followed him upon white _____ . (Rev. 19:14)
43. An afternoon social event.
45. Now the end of the _____ is charity. (1 Tim. 1:5)
50. The children of Lod, Hadid, and _____ . (Ezra 2:33)
52. French for "father."
53. Lamb's alias.
54. _____ [2 words] the true vine. (John 15:1)

55. Medieval lyric poems.
56. Nought.
57. Alkaline caustic.
58. Historical time periods.
59. Scottish for "sly."

Down

1. Eucalyptus secretion.
2. The earth shall weep and mourn _____ her. (Rev. 18:11)
3. I am the _____ , ye are the branches. (John 15:5)
4. The _____ shall serve the younger. (Rom. 9:12)
5. _____ such there is no law. (Gal. 5:23)
6. They were stoned, they were _____ asunder. (Heb. 11:37)
7. Why _____ ye? Rise and pray. (Luke 22:46)
8. He lodgeth with one Simon a _____ (Acts 10:6)
9. _____ my bonds. (Col. 4:18)
10. Rosary bead.
11. The kingdom of heaven is like unto a _____ . (Matt. 13:47)
19. Extinct bird.
20. Edible crustacean.
23. Variant of -able.
24. _____ we all come in the unity. (Eph. 4:13)
25. Whip.
26. St. _____'s fire.
27. The Lamb shall _____ them. (Rev. 17:14)
29. Old Arabic measure.
32. Wherefore _____ we pray always for you. (2 Thess. 1:11)
34. For God is my _____ . (Rom. 1:9)
37. For ye are the _____ of the living God. (2 Cor. 6:16)
39. He _____ captivity captive. (Eph. 4:8)

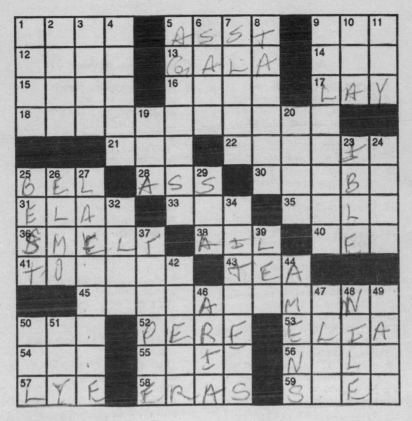

42. Smudge or blot.
44. So be its.
46. Operatic solo.
47. Hebrew month.
48. Egyptian river.
49. We spend our years as a _____ that is told. (Ps. 90:9)

50. Hurt not the _____ and the wine. (Rev. 6:6).
51. _____, I had not known sin. (Rom. 7:7)

4

Across

1. Turban, fez, or bowler.
4. For this _____ is mount Sinai. (Gal. 4:25)
8. But be _____ with sandals. (Mark 6:9)
12. He planteth an _____, and the rain doth nourish it. (Isa. 44:14)
13. For ye _____ up the kingdom of heaven against men. (Matt. 23:13)
14. Learn first to shew piety at _____. (1 Tim. 5:4)
15. Direction from Jerusalem to Masada.
16. Solitary.
17. Babylonian god of war.
18. For my sake this great _____ is upon you. (Jonah 1:12)
20. Location of Tarshish.
21. To soak flax.
22. . . . the son of _____, which was the son of Noe. (Luke 3:36)
23. Single-masted sailboat.
26. For thou, O Lord, hast done as it _____ thee. (Jonah 1:14)
30. Long narrative poem.
31. Let them turn every one from his evil _____. (Jonah 3:8)
32. They shall have like portions to eat, beside that which cometh of the _____ of his patrimony. (Deut. 18:8)
33. All thy _____ and thy waves passed over me. (Jonah 2:3)
35. A fashion or manner.
36. "The Lion of God."
37. Behold, the third _____ cometh quickly. (Rev. 11:14)
38. Jesse's son.
41. Nineveh was an exceeding great city of three days' _____. (Jonah 3:3)

45. As in _____ all die. (1 Cor. 15:22)
46. A word denoting a person, place, or thing.
47. Adam called his wife's name _____. (Gen. 3:20)
48. Connecticut university.
49. Scottish for "old age."
50. Arise, and take up thy _____. (Mark 2:9)
51. Their feet are swift to _____ blood. (Rom. 3:15)
52. Conclusions.
53. Town six miles southeast of Joppa. (Neh. 6:2)

Down

1. Why _____ thou done this? (Jonah 1:10)
2. Hartebeeste.
3. To go with _____ unto Tarshish. (Jonah 1:3)
4. And he lay, and was fast _____. (Jonah 1:5)
5. Then Abraham gave up the _____. (Gen. 25:8)
6. Thou shalt not approach to his wife; she is thine _____. (Lev. 18:14)
7. Cartographer's abbreviation.
8. The _____ came to him, and said unto him, "What meanest thou, O sleeper?" (Jonah 1:6)
9. Israeli dance.
10. Sixth king of Israel
11. College official.
19. So the people of Nineveh believed God, and _____ a fast. (Jonah 3:5)
20. And sat under it in the shadow, till he might _____ what would become of the city. (Jonah 4:5)
22. _____ like a fox.
23. Egyptian earth god.

24. Typesetter's abbreviation.
25. The _____ of joy for mourning. (Isa. 61:3)
26. Dance step.
27. "I _____ unto you."
28. Wing of a building.
29. River at Balmoral Castle.
31. World War I (abbrev.).
34. That _____ serpent, called the Devil. (Rev. 12:9)
35. Except they give a distinction in the _____ . (1 Cor. 14:7)
37. God repented of the evil, that he had said that he _____ do unto them. (Jonah 3:10)

38. Yet forty _____ , and Nineveh shall be overthrown. (Jonah 3:4)
39. Mother of Jabal and Jubal.
40. So he sent him out of the _____ of Hebron. (Gen. 37:14)
41. Let us _____ ourselves to the LORD. (Jer. 50:5)
42. Where Moses viewed the Promised Land.
43. I do well to be angry, _____ unto death. (Jonah 4:9)
44. Former name of Tokyo.
46. Indicator of maiden name.

5

Across

1. City south of Hebron.
5. First king of Israel.
9. The trees of the LORD are full of _____ . (Ps. 104:16)
12. Hindu outer garment.
13. Feminine name.
14. A servant of Solomon.
15. Nebuchadnezzar's title (2 words).
18. Large vessel used to hold liquids.
19. Indefinite periods of time.
20. Therefore _____ I to them in parables. (Matt. 13:13)
23. Trite or commonplace.
25. Third son of Leah.
26. David's tribe.
27. Chemical symbol for iron.
29. Sir, come down _____ my child die. (John 4:49)
30. Abraham's wife.
31. Dicken's pen name.
32. Let us build with you, for _____ seek your God. (Ezra 4:2)
33. Confused noise or hum (of voices or insects).
34. Of the tribe of _____ were sealed twelve thousand. (Rev. 7:6)
35. Restores to health.
36. Son of Jether and Abigail.
37. Religious images.
39. Oklahoma city.
40. He tried to stop Ezra from rebuilding the temple.
46. Malayan gibbon.
47. Killed by a certain man's arrow, dogs licked his blood. (1 Kings 22:37–38)
48. To exchange labor for salary.
49. Bitter vetch.
50. Island off Scotland.
51. College official.

Down

1. At that day ye shall _____ in my name. (John 16:26)
2. Area measurement in Siam.
3. Scottish alder.
4. Father of Uthai and Zabbub.
5. That he may _____ you as wheat. (Luke 22:31)
6. Priestly garment.
7. United States of America (abbrev.).
8. His children returned with Ezra. (Ezra 2:45)
9. Chemical compound.
10. Fifteenth king of Judah.
11. The mantles, and the wimples, and the crisping _____ . (Isa. 3:22)
16. Absalom hanged in an _____ . (2 Sam. 18:10)
17. Informal form of yes.
20. He _____ me not from the womb. (Jer. 20:17)
21. French for "Papa."
22. She was made from Adam's rib.
23. Whirring sounds.
24. First man.
26. Place of legal confinement.
27. Until I make thy _____ thy footstool. (Acts 2:35)
28. Old Testament book about the return of the Jews from Babylon.
30. Son of Bani.
31. Scouting initials.
33. 1/100 of the U.S. dollar.
34. When they beheld him, were greatly _____ . (Mark 9:15)
35. Users of hoes.
36. Why make ye this _____ , and weep? (Mark 5:39)
37. A small island.
38. Troutlike fish.
39. _____ , Father, all things are possible unto thee. (Mark 14:36)

41. Finnish clearing.

42. And the damsel _____ , and told them of her mother's house. (Gen. 24:28)

43. Scottish negative.

44. Son of Jether.

45. There was no room for them in the _____ . (Luke 2:7)

6

Across

1. Small, winged, biting insect.
5. He planteth an _____ . (Isa. 44:14)
8. South African weaverbird.
12. They sang together by course in praising and giving thanks _____ the LORD. (Ezra 3:11)
13. Indicator of maiden name.
14. Hebrew name.
15. Teenager.
16. Pedagogues.
18. South American Indian groups.
20. Woman's name.
21. To contend or dispute.
24. For our God is a consuming _____ . (Heb. 12:29)
25. Number of ungrateful lepers.
26. He is a _____ of God. (Rom. 13:4)
30. Large bird.
31. Feudal lord.
32. Scottish explorer.
33. Cowboy films.
35. Tablelike hill.
36. Mild oath.
37. Simon, who is called _____ . (Matt. 10:2)
38. Of or pertaining to Moses.
41. Purpose or goal.
42. Those who are sent forth.
44. To be an omen of.
48. But the tongue can no man _____ . (James 3:8)
49. Distinctive time period.
50. The land of Nod, on the east of _____ . (Gen. 4:16)
51. The love of God is _____ abroad. (Rom. 5:5)
52. Draft organization.
53. Will _____ the caul of their heart. (Hos. 13:8)

Down

1. To destroy the interior of.
2. Direction from Jerusalem to Tiberias.
3. I _____ no pleasant bread. (Dan. 10:3)
4. Every _____ should confess that Jesus Christ is Lord. (Phil. 2:11)
5. The _____ are a people not strong. (Prov. 30:25)
6. Now we _____ through a glass, darkly. (1 Cor. 13:12)
7. Cures.
8. Giggles in a silly manner.
9. The blood of righteous _____ . (Matt. 23:35)
10. Barb of a feather.
11. Loop or structure resembling a loop.
17. Discoverer of polonium and radium.
19. Electrical engineer (abbrev.).
21. Again.
22. Hoarfrost.
23. Wildebeests.
24. A diabolically evil person.
26. Unexplainable events.
27. Allowance of weight added to various commodities.
28. Woe to them that are at _____ in Zion. (Amos 6:1)
29. Wilt thou _____ it up in three days? (John 2:20)
31. Legitimate (slang).
34. Vexed or coaxed.
35. For the body is not one _____ . (1 Cor. 12:14)
37. Sixteenth letter of the Greek alphabet.
38. Thickly tangled masses.
39. Brightly colored fish.
40. That I might by all means save _____ . (1 Cor. 9:22)

41. _____ heart was perfect. (1 Kings 15:14)
43. Bitter vetch.
45. Lyrical poem.

46. But ye have made it a _____ of thieves. (Matt. 21:13)
47. Whose _____ shall be according to their works. (2 Cor. 11:15)

7

Across

1. Adapts or suits.
5. In her mouth was an olive _____ . (Gen. 8:11)
9. And cried with a loud _____ to him that had the sharp sickle. (Rev. 14:18)
12. To the seven churches which are in _____ . (Rev. 1:4)
13. Feminine nickname.
14. Scottish for "grandchild."
15. Last book of the New Testament (2 words).
18. Gods (Latin, plural).
19. Rips or tears.
20. Center of the iris (of the eye).
23. Gradually decreases.
25. These are the two anointed _____ . (Zech. 4:14)
26. Spanish bowling.
27. Their works _____ follow them. (Rev. 14:13)
29. Stationary (abbrev.).
30. To explode.
31. There was seen in his temple the _____ of his testament. (Rev. 11:19)
32. I Jesus have sent mine angel _____ testify unto you. (Rev. 22:16)
33. Whirls.
34. And the name of the _____ is called Wormwood. (Rev. 8:11)
35. The dromedaries of Midian and _____ . (Isa. 60:6)
36. I am Alpha and _____ . (Rev. 1:11)
37. Hindu princess.
39. Quality (comb. form).
40. The Revelation _____ [3 words]. (Rev. 1:1)
46. Former Chinese leader.
47. Elementary constituent of a whole.
48. Born (Old English).
49. To inquire closely.
50. Beloved, now are we the _____ of God. (1 John 3:2)
51. Jesus Christ be with you all. _____ . (Rev. 22:21)

Down

1. The liberal soul shall be made _____ . (Prov. 11:25)
2. Hebrew for "man."
3. And _____ the kine to the cart. (1 Sam. 6:7)
4. Fifth Asian church. (Rev. 3:1)
5. Another name for Matthew.
6. Adam's wife.
7. To feel ill.
8. _____ ; [2 words] I am the first and the last. (Rev. 1:17)
9. Metal money.
10. Indian peasant.
11. Japanese coins.
16. Snakelike fish.
17. Golf accessories.
20. Now my days are swifter than a _____ . (Job 9:25)
21. For I testify _____ every man that heareth. (Rev. 22:18)
22. Round, edible seed from a pod.
23. His deadly _____ was healed. (Rev. 13:3)
24. South-central European mountains.
26. Vigor.
27. And burn incense unto their _____ . (Hab. 1:16)
28. Gumbo vegetable.
30. First Asian church. (Rev. 2:1)
31. I took the little book out of the angel's hand, and _____ it up. (Rev. 10:10)
33. Graf _____ , a German Ship.
34. Second Asian church. (Rev. 2:8)

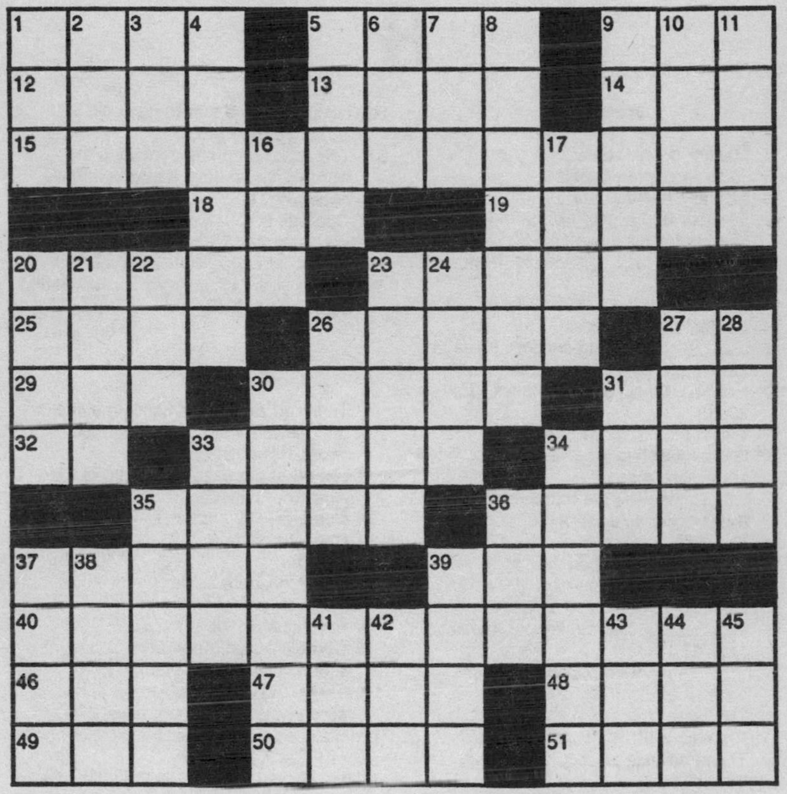

35. To eat and to drink, and to ______ the good of all his labour. (Eccles. 5:18)
36. Used to express regret or surprise.
37. To frolic boisterously.
38. As many as trade by sea, stood ______ off. (Rev. 18:17)
39. Praise him for his mighty ______. (Ps. 150:2)
41. One (Spanish).
42. ______ lieth at the door. (Gen. 4:7)
43. ______ [2 words] the door of the sheep. (John 10:7)
44. Abbreviation for a female saint.
45. Ye shall have tribulation ______ days. (Rev. 2:10)

8

Across

1. Manner or method.
5. To show or plan in detail.
8. Mentally healthy.
12. The four and twenty elders and the four beasts fell down and worshipped . . . saying, _____; Alleluia. (Rev. 19:4)
13. Spanish cheer.
14. Contest or trial (Greek).
15. _____ , be of good comfort; thy faith hath made thee whole. (Matt. 9:22)
17. Even so, come, _____ Jesus. (Rev. 22:20)
18. Within (comb. form).
19. Suffix indicating a native or resident of a specified place.
20. _____ shewed me a pure river of water of life. (Rev. 22:1)
21. The self.
22. _____ for her, when they shall see the smoke of her burning. (Rev. 18:9)
26. He buildeth his house as a moth, and as a _____ that the keeper maketh. (Job 27:18)
29. When Isaac was old, and his eyes were _____ . (Gen. 27:1)
30. The letter ρ.
31. Aramaic word for "father."
32. These sayings _____ faithful and true. (Rev. 22:6)
33. Saul's body hung on the wall of Beth-_____ , (1 Sam. 31:10)
34. Female deer.
35. Fated to die soon (Scottish).
36. I, John, saw these things, and _____ them. (Rev. 22:8)
37. The four and twenty _____ . (Rev. 19:4)
39. In righteousness he doth judge and make _____ . (Rev. 19:11)
40. The gates of it shall not be shut at all _____ day. (Rev. 21:25)
41. I would thou wert cold or _____ . (Rev. 3:15)
42. Mineral spring.
45. _____ Domini.
48. Prophet son of Hilkiah.

50. I will cause the sun to go down at _____ . (Amos 8:9)
51. The _____ commandment is the word which ye have heard from the beginning. (1 John 2:7)
52. Operatic solo.
53. Weak-minded (South).
54. Bureau of Labor Statistics (abbrev.).
55. I have given you every _____ bearing seed. (Gen. 1:29)

Down

1. The marriage of the Lamb is come, and his wife hath _____ herself ready. (Rev. 19:7)
2. Nation at the easternmost tip of the Arabian peninsula.
3. Deuteronomy (abbrev.).
4. Phonetic symbol.
5. Maxim.
6. To the sheltered side.
7. Through, or according to.
8. Melchizedek, king of _____ .
9. Cornelius said, Four days _____ I was fasting. (Acts 10:30)
10. There shall be no more death, neither sorrow, _____ crying. (Rev. 21:4)
11. But the _____ of all things is at hand. (1 Peter 4:7)
16. He carried me away in the spirit to a great and _____ mountain. (Rev. 21:10)
20. Youngest son of Noah.
21. Seventh Greek letter.
22. No _____ is of the truth. (1 John 2:21)
23. Hebrew measure.
24. I will come _____ to you to judgment. (Mal. 3:5)
25. The thoughts of the diligent _____ only to plenteousness. (Prov. 21:5)
26. The spirit _____ me go with them. (Acts 11:12)
27. Ancient Greek coin.
28. Child of Boaz and Ruth.
29. O ye _____ bones. (Ezek. 37:4)
32. Plural of a.
33. To be (Spanish).

18

35. Newly hatched fish.
36. These shall _____ the whore. (Rev. 17:16)
38. They brought thee for a present horns of ivory and _____ . (Ezek. 27:15)
39. Write: for these _____ are true and faithful. (Rev. 21:5)
41. Death and _____ were cast into the lake of fire. (Rev. 20:14)
42. Male parent of an animal.

43. And he that sat on him had a _____ of balances in his hand. (Rev. 6:5)
44. Seventh king of Israel (873–851 B.C.).
45. The Spirit _____ the bride say, Come. (Rev. 22:17)
46. Scottish dialect for "now."
47. See thou do it _____ , for I am thy fellowservant. (Rev. 22:9)
48. Shortest book title in the Bible.
49. Mahogany (abbrev.).

9

Across

1. There shall come in the last
   _____ scoffers. (2 Peter 3:3)
5. Than (German).
8. Exact copies (slang).
12. Electrical (abbrev.).
13. Mahogany (abbrev.).
14. One of David's mighty men.
    (1 Chron. 11:29)
15. Is blind and cannot see _____
    off. (2 Peter 1:9)
16. Plural of os (mouth).
17. That it _____ not in the days of
    their prophecy. (Rev. 11:6)
18. Son of Ahasuerus.
20. Coloring.
22. College degree.
23. Standing room only (abbrev.).
24. An assistant.
27. Ancient Babylonian.
31. Stationary (abbrev.).
32. As a _____ of corn cometh in in
    his season. (Job 5:26)
33. Gone by; past.
34. One of Daniel's Hebrew friends.
35. Her adversary also provoked her
    sore, for to make her _____.
    (1 Sam. 1:6)
36. Wing of a building.
37. Short, informal greeting.
38. And had _____ down manna
    upon them to eat. (Ps. 78:24)
42. Belteshazzar.
46. French for "angel."
47. Asahel was as light of foot as a
    wild _____. (2 Sam. 2:18)
49. If an ox _____ a man or a
    woman. (Exod. 21:28)
50. An act intended to deceive or to
    trick.
51. Direction from Jerusalem to
    Jericho.
52. Noun suffix.

53. He slew of Edom in the valley of
    _____ ten thousand. (2 Kings
    14:7)
54. In the land of _____ , on the east
    of Eden. (Gen. 4:16)
55. Scottish shipyards.

Down

1. Ready to judge the quick and the
   _____ . (1 Peter 4:5)
2. Military code word.
3. His parents went to Jerusalem
   every _____ . (Luke 2:41)
4. Where is the wise? Where is the
   _____ ? (1 Cor 1:20)
5. Thus _____ saith, Jeroboam
   shall die by the sword. (Amos
   7:11)
6. Tutelary deity of ancient Rome.
7. One of the Hebrews saved from
   the fiery furnace.
8. How great a matter a little _____
   kindleth! (James 3:5)
9. Russian mountain range.
10. Older brother of Abel.
11. Spring up, O well; _____ ye into
    it. (Num. 21:17)
19. That hath called _____ to glory
    and virtue. (2 Peter 1:3)
21. Yellow portion of an egg.
23. Sandbank or sandbar.
24. He planteth an _____ , and the
    rain doth nourish it. (Isa. 44:14)
25. A Philippine people.
26. Son of Jacob not mentioned in
    the New Testament.
27. As obedient _____ , not
    fashioning yourselves according
    to the former lusts. (1 Peter 1:14)
28. Hear this, ye old men, and give
    _____ . (Joel 1:2)
29. He is of _____ ; ask him. (John
    9:21)

1	2	3	4	■	5	6	7	■	8	9	10	11
12				■	13			■	14			
15				■	16			■	17			
18				19		■	20	21				
■		22			■	23			■	■	■	■
24	25	26		■	27				■	28	29	30
31			■	32				■	33			
34						■		35				
■				36			■	37		■	■	■
38	39	40	41			■	42			43	44	45
46			■	47	48			49				
50			■	51				■	52			
53			■	54				■	55			

30. For we have _____ followed cunningly devised fables. (2 Peter 1:16)
32. Large knife.
35. I with the _____ of God cast out devils. (Luke 11:20)
37. _____ ; and he smelleth the battle afar off. (Job 39:25)
38. College cheers.
39. Small buffalo.
40. One of David's mighty men. (2 Sam. 23:36)

41. Let us go into the _____ towns. (Mark 1:38)
42. What _____ is this that ye have done? (Gen. 44:15)
43. Island near Scotland.
44. Irish Gaelic.
45. A feast of wines on the _____. (Isa. 25:6)
48. The children of Lod, Hadid, and _____ . (Neh. 7:37)

10

Across

1. South African fox.
5. David said unto _____, I am in a great strait. (2 Sam. 24:14)
8. Pulpy fruit residue.
12. Lounge around.
13. Praise him, _____ ye stars of light. (Ps. 148:3)
14. Lamb's alias.
15. At _____, we were bold in our God. (1 Thess. 2:2)
17. It is turned as clay to the _____. (Job 38:14)
18. Therefore (German).
19. For he flattereth _____ in his own eyes. (Ps. 36:2)
21. _____ a watch, O LORD, before my mouth. (Ps. 141:3)
23. Uzziel, and Jerimoth, and _____. (1 Chron 7:7)
24. I have not _____ with vain persons. (Ps. 26:4)
27. O ye sons of _____ how long will ye turn my glory into shame? (Ps. 4:2)
29. The daughter of Asher was _____. (Num. 26:46)
33. To send forth.
35. To propose or intend.
37. Israeli dance.
38. _____ the Morashtite prophesied. (Jer. 26:18)
40. Saccharine source.
42. Chemical abbreviation.
43. Reign; rule (Hindu).
45. Let them make a noise like a _____. (Ps. 59:14)
47. We are _____ as sheep for the slaughter. (Ps. 44:22)
51. I am like a green _____ tree in the house of God. (Ps. 52:8)
55. Latin for "lambs."
56. He _____ no man to do them wrong. (Ps. 105:14)
58. The iniquity of _____ house shall not be purged. (1 Sam. 3:14)
59. _____ hospitality one to another. (1 Peter 4:9)
60. Dry.
61. _____ Antilles (abbrev.)
62. Enclosure for swine.
63. The LORD is upon _____ waters. (Ps. 29:3)

Down

1. European mountain system.
2. London district.
3. Slight in girth.
4 English psychologist Havelock _____.
5. Stand in the _____ before me for the land. (Ezek. 22:30)
6. River in *Kubla Khan*.
7. 553 (Roman num.).
8. Build Jerusalem unto the _____ the Prince. (Dan. 9:25)
9. At the leeward side.
10. Basic monetary unit of Iran.
11. He maketh them also to skip like a _____. (Ps. 29:6)
16. Single unit in a collection.
20. Matron's title.
22. Bitter beverage.
24. Arphaxad, which was the son of _____. (Luke 3:36)
25. Zebaim, the children of _____. (Ezra 2:57)
26. Facial spasm.
28. Egg of a louse.
30. To decompose.
31. Blessed _____ all they that put their trust in him. (Ps. 2:12)
32. Jacob sojourned in the land of _____. (Ps. 105:23)
34. To make dull.
36. They that are _____ against me are sworn against me. (Ps. 102:8)

39. Headwear.
41. Let my tongue cleave to the
    _____ of my mouth. (Ps. 137:6)
44. Even so, come, Lord _____ .
    (Rev. 22:20)
46. To glow.
47. Orne River city.
48. Amorous leer.

49. Elementary constituent of a
    whole.
50. I beat them small as the _____
    before the wind. (Ps. 18:42)
52. Babylonian war god.
53. Surely there is a _____ for the
    silver. (Job 28:1)
54. Whirlpool.
57. Enchanted (Scottish).

11

Across

1. The press is full, the _____ overflow. (Joel 3:13)
5. Anna, the prophetess, was of the tribe of _____ . (Luke 2:36)
9. Affirmative vote.
12. Operatic solo.
13. I have remembered thy _____ , O Lord. (Ps. 119:55)
14. Regular (abbrev.).
15. Thou hast _____ us to keep thy precepts diligently. (Ps. 119:4)
17. Give _____ to my words, O Lord. (Ps. 5:1)
18. To feel faint from the heat.
19. An half _____ of land, which a yoke of oxen might plow. (1 Sam. 14:14)
20. Duck genus.
21. Both were cast alive into a _____ of fire. (Rev. 19:20)
23. Twentieth Hebrew letter.
26. Our soul is _____ as a bird out of the snare. (Ps. 124:7)
29. Go to the _____ , thou sluggard. (Prov. 6:6)
30. Author of the *Divine Comedy.*
32. Twenty-second Hebrew letter.
33. Her bowels _____ upon her son. (1 Kings 3:26)
35. This (Spanish).
36. Lest he _____ my soul like a lion. (Ps. 7:2)
37. Scottish alder.
39. My _____ hath kept thy testimonies. (Ps. 119:167)
41. Mine _____ have forgotten thy words. (Ps. 119:139)
45. His strange work; and bring to pass his _____ . (Isa. 28:21)
46. Teach me good _____ [plural] and knowledge. (Ps. 119:66)
48. A Shoshonean Indian.
49. As he saith also in _____ , I will call them my people. (Rom. 9:25)
50. He _____ redemption unto his people. (Ps. 111:9)
51. Alamos or Angeles.
52. A _____ and a pomegranate. (Exo. 39:26)
53. Pertaining to a Babylonian god.

Down

1. Decorative letters (abbrev.).
2. There was _____ [2 words] of building round about in them. (Ezek. 46:23)
3. It is _____ for thee, Lord, to work. (Ps. 119:126)
4. King of Edom.
5. A supplementary structure.
6. Lotus tree.
7. Crony or gossip.
8. There is a cup, and the wine is _____ . (Ps. 75:8)
9. I will meditate in thy _____ . (Ps. 119:15)
10. Go up, _____ an altar unto the Lord. (2 Sam. 24:18)
11. Monster.
16. I _____ no pleasant bread. (Dan. 10:3)
19. Alias initials.
21. Military landing craft.
22. Top gun or top card.
23. Cowfish.
24. Direction from Jerusalem to Jericho.
25. I will keep thy _____ : O forsake me not. (Ps. 119:8)
26. I have seen an _____ of all perfection. (Ps. 119:96)
27. Man did _____ angels' food. (Ps. 78:25)
28. Give them their meat in _____ season. (Ps. 104:27)
30. Deoxyribonucleic acid.

31. Chalice veil.
34. Unit of electrical reluctance.
35. To entangle in a net.
37. Let the _____ of the LORD chase them. (Ps. 35:5)
38. Deep sleep indicator.
39. Ramah is afraid; Gibeah of _____ is fled. (Isa. 10:29)
40. Eight's prefix

41. Noble (German).
42. Arrow poison.
43. Mediterranean volcano.
44. Fastest commercial carriers.
46. For _____ has said, I am righteous. (Job 34:5)
47. Neither shall ye _____ enchantment. (Lev. 19:26)

12

Across

1. The flesh of an adult bovine.
5. Upon or over.
9. Jewish teacher's title.
12. Israel journeyed, and spread his tent beyond the tower of _____. (Gen. 35:21)
13. Sages.
14. Sooner or before.
15. Air (comb. form).
16. Ye have lived in _____ on the earth. (James 5:5)
18. Detangle from a seine.
20. I have _____ him to the LORD. (1 Sam. 1:28)
21. Birthname indicator.
23. For godly _____ worketh repentance to salvation. (2 Cor. 7:10)
27. Mine own mouth shall _____ me. (Job 9:20)
31. The scripture was fulfilled which _____, Abraham believed God. (James 2:23)
32. Irish indeed!
33. Is not this he that _____ and begged? (John 9:8)
35. Lest ye fall _____ condemnation (James 5:12)
36. Cram or plug.
38. Heirs of the _____ which he hath promised. (James 2:5)
40. But the _____ can no man tame. (James 3:8)
42. Expression of contempt.
43. Wide-mouthed vessel.
45. Not fresh.
49. Seem to be religious, and _____ not his tongue. (James 1:26)
53. Small brown bird.
54. All that handle the _____ , the mariners. (Ezek. 27:29)
55. The days of _____ were nine hundred and five years. (Gen. 5:11)
56. Of Sallai, Kallai; of _____ , Eber. (Neh. 12:20)
57. Ceremonial wine cup.
58. Make a long blast with the _____ horn. (Josh. 6:5)
59. Tanager.

Down

1. Dandy.
2. Nod, on the east of _____. (Gen. 4:16)
3. Deserve by merit.
4. He [Abraham] was called the _____ [3 words]. (James 2:23)
5. Unit of electrical intensity (abbrev.).
6. I will cut down the _____ cedars. (Isa. 37:24)
7. Pointed arches.
8. Felt-hammered, steel-stringed instruments.
9. Son of Peleg.
10. Do not _____ , my beloved brethren. (James 1:16)
11. Honey-producing insect.
17. And _____ forgetteth what manner of man he was. (James 1:24)
19. Peg used to elevate a golf ball.
22. German spa town.
24. Hard outer layer.
25. Flower extract for perfume.
26. With _____ there is no variableness. (James 1:17)
27. The great dragon was _____ out. (Rev. 12:9)
28. Not to Abraham, _____ [2 words] his seed. (Rom. 4:13)
29. Substantive word.
30. Point or end.

34. Put it upon the _____ of the right ear. (Exod. 29:20)
37. As no _____ on earth can white them. (Mark 9:3)
39. Latin pronoun (plural).
41. Diminutive form of Helena.
44. Indivisible particle.
46. Weapon (French).

47. Ponce de _____ .
48. Babylonian deity.
49. Scarf.
50. I saw the _____ pushing westward. (Dan. 8:4)
51. _____ the son of Ikkesh the Tekoite. (2 Sam. 23:26)
52. Fellow of the historical society.

13

Across

1. Peter having a sword _____ it. (John 18:10)
5. _____, which was the son of Noe. (Luke 3:36)
8. Chemical salts.
12. He denied with an _____, I do not know the man. (Matt. 26:72)
13. Extravehicular activity (abbrev.).
14. Prepare for publication.
15. This (Spanish).
16. Odd's opposite (poetic).
17. Woe to them that are at _____ in Zion. (Amos 6:1)
18. At that day ye _____ [3 words]. (John 14:20)
21. Expression of contempt.
22. Alkali.
23. Arab overcoat.
26. My head with _____ thou didst not anoint. (Luke 7:46)
28. Closely or tightly (Latin).
32. 18 across continued (6 words).
36. Most important.
37. Except ye _____ the flesh of the Son of man. (John 6:53)
38. All that handle the _____, the mariners. (Ezek. 27:29)
39. Italian monk.
42. Married woman's title.
44. 18 across continued, with "and ye" (6 words).
51. Speaker's platform.
52. _____ his son, Jehoshuah his son. (1 Chron. 7:27)
53. Longest division of geological time.
54. Fluff or fuzz.
55. Every _____ that doeth evil hateth the light. (John 3:20)
56. Indian princess.
57. Kneads bread (Scottish).
58. _____, Lord: yet the dogs under the table eat of the children's crumbs. (Mark 7:28)
59. He was (Latin).

Down

1. Third-person singular present tense of "do."
2. Be not _____ with thy mouth. (Eccles. 5:2)
3. Henrietta's pet name.
4. Judah is a lion's _____. (Gen. 49:9)
5. The hand of our God is upon all them for good that _____ [2 words]. (Ezra 8:22)
6. We have one Father, _____ God. (John 8:41)
7. Main house on an estate.
8. _____ [2 words] no man know it. (Matt. 9:30)
9. One of Esau's wives.
10. Nickname for Elizabeth.
11. Word in a printer's proof.
19. Northern diving bird.
20. _____ beheld his glory. (John 1:14)
23. To direct or intend.
24. Bleat.
25. The children of Pochereth of Zebaim, the children of _____. (Ezra 2:57)
27. Strong alkaline solution.
29. Seventeenth Greek letter.
30. Asian evergreen shrub.
31. Ye do _____, not knowing the scriptures. (Matt. 22:29)
33. Overruns.
34. There shall be _____, and pestilences. (Matt. 24:7)
35. Son of Brahma.
40. Sun god.
41. To bother or molest.

43. Let their table be made a _____ . (Rom. 11:9)
44. Every _____ word that men shall speak, they shall give account thereof. (Matt. 12:36)
45. To leave us a remnant to escape, and to give us a _____ in his holy place. (Ezra 9:8)
46. Ye tithe _____ and rue and all manner of herbs. (Luke 11:42)
47. And he said unto me, It is _____ . (Rev. 21:6)
48. Lord, let it alone this _____ also. (Luke 13:8)
49. Charlie Chaplin's wife.
50. A constituent of the whole.

14

Across

1. The children of Ezer are these; Bilhan, and Zaavan, and _____. (Gen. 36:27)
5. Wondrous works in the land of _____. (Ps. 106:22)
8. They made the _____, which Aaron made. (Exod. 32:35)
12. Demonstration (abbrev.).
13. How long is it _____ since this came unto him? (Mark 9:21)
14. Relating to the mouth.
15. For I am the least of the _____. (1 Cor. 15:9)
17. Call me not Naomi, call me _____. (Ruth 1:20)
18. Greedy person.
19. Now the coat was without _____. (John 19:23)
21. The king of _____ in the coast of _____. (Josh. 12:23)
23. To be frightened.
27. World War II site.
30. Thy god, O _____, liveth. (Amos 8:14)
32. A friend of the world is the _____ of God. (James 4:4)
33. The _____ of the wicked shall be broken. (Ps. 37:17)
35. Jacob's seventh son.
37. Ten cent coin.
38. She [Jezebel] painted her face, and _____ her head. (2 Kings 9:30)
40. And _____ shall wipe away all tears from their eyes. (Rev. 7:17)
42. Be not as the hypocrites, of a _____ countenance. (Matt. 6:16)
43. My _____ shall not always strive with man. (Gen. 6:3)
45. To _____, that God was in Christ. (2 Cor. 5:19)
47. The _____ of the temple was rent in twain. (Mark 15:38)
49. Pert.
53. Information.
56. The _____ is not above his master. (Matt. 10:24)
58. _____ so, come Lord Jesus. (Rev. 22:20)
59. Pochereth of Zebaim, the children of _____. (Ezra 2:57)
60. Make ready; for these men shall dine with me at _____. (Gen. 43:16)
61. Fools die for _____ of wisdom. (Prov. 10:21)
62. _____ him eschew evil, and do good. (1 Peter 3:11)
63. Explosives.

Down

1. First man.
2. Military cap.
3. _____, which was the son of Naum. (Luke 3:25)
4. Scented.
5. Harold's nickname.
6. Which in other _____ was not made known unto the sons of men. (Eph. 3:5)
7. Contending with the devil he disputed about the body of _____. (Jude 9)
8. These things _____ and teach. (1 Tim. 4:11)
9. Sons of Jether; Jephunneh, and Pispah, and _____. (1 Chron. 7:38)
10. Malayan gibbon.
11. Florida (abbrev.).
16. Will you keep to the old path that evil men have _____? (Job 22:15, NIV)
20. High card.
22. Syncopated music.
24. Moslem chief.
25. Woman's name.
26. Colored.

27. The man who _____ everything must not look down on him who does not. (Rom. 14:3, NIV)
28. Voyage or journey.
29. Ahab, the son of _____. (1 Kings 16:30)
31. Aged, unsound horse.
34. No _____ can serve two masters. (Luke 16:13)
36. Endow (archaic).
39. It is appointed unto men once to _____. (Heb. 9:27)
41. Circular plate.
44. _____ king of nations. (Gen. 14:1)
46. Affect slightly and unpleasantly.

48. He burned the bones of the king of Edom into _____. (Amos 2:1)
50. On the surface.
51. Coagulated mass.
52. Longings.
53. My head is filled with _____. (Song of Sol. 5:2)
54. Men from Babylon, and from Cuthah, and from _____. (2 Kings 17:24)
55. Ye shall have tribulation _____ days. (Rev. 2:10)
57. Made us _____ together in heavenly places in Christ Jesus. (Eph. 2:6)

31

15

Across

1. They do alway _____ in their heart. (Heb. 3:10)
4. Fine-grained mineral.
8. _____ and his wife hid themselves from the presence of the LORD God. (Gen. 3:8)
12. Sixteenth English letter.
13. Aroma or scent.
14. As a _____ is full of birds, so are their houses full of deceit. (Jer. 5:27)
15. Isaiah (abbrev.).
16. Assistant.
17. Jogging gait.
18. The disciples were called _____ first in Antioch. (Acts 11:26)
21. Holy ones or roads.
22. Come ye _____ the waters. (Isa. 55:1)
23. His [Hezekiah's] mother's name also was _____. (2 Kings 18:2)
26. Pollute ye my holy name no more with your gifts, and with your _____. (Ezek. 20:39)
29. _____ if I make you sorry, who is he then that maketh me glad? (2 Cor. 2:2)
30. Babylon is taken, _____ is confounded. (Jer. 50:2)
31. _____ it, even to the foundation. (Ps. 137:7)
32. The tenth part of a bath out of the _____. (Ezek. 45:14)
33. By faith _____ offered unto God a more excellent sacrifice. (Heb. 11:4)
34. I _____ no pleasant bread. (Dan. 10:3)
35. Upon the great _____ of his right foot. (Lev. 8:23)
36. I am become as sounding _____. (1 Cor. 13:1)
37. Fourth English letter.

38. Hindu mantra.
39. Large extinct bird.
40. Pledge or vow.
45. Thought or notion.
48. Mother's sister.
49. To strive or compete.
50. _____, also, who received tithes. (Heb. 7:9)
51. Little boy (Spanish).
52. There was no room for them in the _____. (Luke 2:7)
53. Though ye have _____ among the pots. (Ps. 68:13)
54. 0.0625 ounce.
55. _____ him take the water. (Rev. 22:17)

Down

1. Extended narrative poem.
2. Twentieth Hebrew letter.
3. Go up, _____ an altar unto the LORD. (2 Sam. 24:18)
4. Warms thoroughly.
5. Mine entrances.
6. Napoleonic victory.
7. Remember now thy _____ in the days of thy youth. (Eccles. 12:1)
8. Praise him for his mighty _____. (Ps. 150:2)
9. Indian timber tree.
10. I knew a man in Christ above fourteen years _____. (2 Cor. 12:2)
11. Jesus _____ them, saying, All hail. (Matt. 28:9)
19. I . . . was in the _____ that is called Patmos. (Rev. 1:9)
20. Neither cold _____ hot. (Rev. 3:16)
23. He said, _____ Father, all things are possible unto thee. (Mark 14:36)
24. They compassed me about like _____. (Ps. 118:12)

1	2	3		4	5	6	7		8	9	10	11
12				13					14			
15				16					17			
18			19					20				
			21				22			23	24	25
26	27	28				29				30		
31					32				33			
34				35				36				
37				38			39					
			40			41				42	43	44
45	46	47		48					49			
50				51					52			
53				54					55			

25. Evils or disasters.
26. Enoch's son. (Gen. 4:18)
27. Palm fruit.
28. He saith also in _____ , I will call them my people. (Rom. 9:25)
29. Opponent or enemy.
32. I _____ thee in the name of Jesus Christ. (Acts 16:18)
33. Esrom begat _____ . (Matt. 1:3)
35. Is any thing _____ hard for the LORD? (Gen. 18:14)
36. They sank into the _____ as a stone. (Exod. 15:5)
39. _____ haha, Hiawatha's flame.

40. And the LORD set a mark upon _____ . (Gen. 4:15)
41. Alaskan glacier or California park.
42. Turn ye now from your _____ ways. (Zech. 1:4)
43. But where are the _____ ? (Luke 17:17)
44. Sarah heard it in the _____ door. (Gen. 18:10)
45. Love worketh no _____ to his neighbour. (Rom. 13:10)
46. Vox populi, vox _____ .
47. Adam was first formed, then _____ . (1 Tim. 2:13)

16

Across

1. I will _____ off from the top of his young twigs. (Ezek. 17:22)
5. If I be wicked, _____ unto me. (Job 10:15)
8. This is that which was spoken by the prophet _____. (Acts 2:16)
12. Japanese bush clover.
13. Then arose Peter, and _____ unto the sepulchre. (Luke 24:12)
14. _____ have I hated. (Rom. 9:13)
15. Donkey (German).
16. Native mineral.
17. Boundary or limit.
18. Now _____ [2 words] of David the king, first and last. (1 Chron. 29:29)
20. Abel was the keeper of _____. (Gen. 4:2)
21. Ball stand or English letter.
22. Was not Abraham _____ father justified by works? (James 2:21)
23. Saw I none, save _____ the Lord's brother. (Gal. 1:19)
26. O _____, keep that which is committed to thy trust. (1 Tim. 6:20)
30. Yet _____ they turned about with a very small helm. (James 3:4)
31. The sun.
32. For ye tithe mint and _____. (Luke 11:42)
33. He saw a man, named _____, sitting at the receipt of custom. (Matt. 9:9)
36. Let not sin therefore _____ in your mortal bodies. (Rom. 6:12)
38. Noah begat Shem, _____, and Japheth. (Gen. 5:32)
39. Snakelike fish.
40. Tell me, what shall thy _____ be? (Gen. 29:15)
43. I will tarry at _____ until Pentecost. (1 Cor. 16:8)
47. Ahab the son of _____ did evil. (1 Kings 16:30)
48. He planteth an _____, and the rain doth nourish it. (Isa. 44:14)
49. Wind direction indicator.
50. We _____ all like bears, and mourn sore like doves. (Isa. 59:11)
51. Before the throne there was a _____ of glass. (Rev. 4:6)
52. Being (Spanish).
53. Obscures.
54. Transliteration of Hebrew *man*.
55. Inert gas used in electric lamps.

Down

1. Nickname for Chester.
2. The heart also of the _____ shall understand knowledge. (Isa. 32:4)
3. S-shaped molding.
4. Whom ye delivered up, and denied him in the presence of _____. (Acts 3:13)
5. I _____ unto you with many tears. (2 Cor. 2:4)
6. Wherein shall go no galley with _____. (Isa. 33:21)
7. Direction from Gaza to Jerusalem.
8. Moses kept the flock of _____. (Exod. 3:1)
9. As he saith also in _____, I will call them my people. (Rom. 9:25)
10. Hearing apparatus (Old English).
11. If the firstfruit be holy, the _____ is also holy. (Rom. 11:16)
19. French pronoun.
20. O God! how great is the _____ of them! (Ps. 139:17)
22. I gave her corn, and wine, and _____. (Hos. 2:8)
23. To wedge or a preserve.
24. Son of Jether. (1 Chron. 7:38)

25. The LORD _____ Balaam, and put a word in his mouth. (Num. 23:16)
26. They are extinct, they are quenched as _____ . (Isa. 43:17)
27. Three or thirds (comb. form).
28. To embrace.
29. Longing.
31. Arphaxad, which was the son of _____ . (Luke 3:36)
34. Whose words shall stand, mine or _____ . (Jer. 44:28)
35. God _____ granted me another child. (Gen. 4:25, NIV)
36. Alkali.

37. Then the _____ disciples went away into Galilee. (Matt. 28:16)
39. This is an _____ that goeth forth. (Zech. 5:6)
40. His name is called The _____ of God. (Rev. 19:13)
41. Mine. (French)
42. One-thousandth of a kilogram.
43. Hungarian rain shower.
44. Mentally sound.
45. Brought them _____ Adam to see what he would call them. (Gen. 2:19)
46. He that doeth evil hath not _____ God. (3 John 11)
48. Samoan mullusk.

17

Across

1. Italian monks.
5. The seven thin ears devoured the seven _____ and full ears. (Gen. 41:7)
9. Given to hospitality, _____ to teach. (1 Tim. 3:2)
12. Go to now, ye _____ men, weep and howl for your miseries. (James 5:1)
13. Hawaiian royalty.
14. Smote them, until they came under Beth-_____ . (1 Sam. 7:11)
15. About the space of two hours cried out, Great is Diana of the _____ . (Acts 19:34)
17. Three (Italian).
18. Golf ball peg.
19. The serpent was more subtil than _____ beast. (Gen. 3:1)
20. The Lord _____ and will not repent. (Heb. 7:21)
22. The _____ , which is strong, and as a molten looking glass. (Job 37:18)
23. Gods (Latin).
24. Facial expression of pleasure.
27. After threescore and two weeks shall _____ be cut off. (Dan. 9:26)
31. Home of Irish kings.
32. Wrath or anger.
33. None is so fierce that _____ stir him up. (Job 41:10)
34. Why do the disciples of John fast often, and make _____ ? (Luke 5:33)
36. Underwater radar system.
37. _____ , lama sabachthani? (Matt. 27:46)
38. Man's name.
39. Girl's nickname.
42. Vase.
43. Musical rest.
46. I took the little book out of the angel's hand, and _____ it up. (Rev. 10:10)
47. But _____ which is above is free. (Gal. 4:26)
50. Deliver thyself as a _____ from the hand of the hunter. (Prov. 6:5)
51. _____ ! for that day is great, so that none is like it. (Jer. 30:7)
52. Agricultural storage structure.
53. Thou sayest that I am a king. To this _____ was I born. (John 18:37)
54. A great multitude of impotent folk, of blind, _____ , withered. (John 5:3)
55. The grace of our Lord Jesus Christ be with you all. _____ . (Rev. 22:21)

Down

1. Thou shalt burn it in the fire; it is _____ inward. (Lev. 13:55)
2. Put ye in the sickle, for the harvest is _____ . (Joel 3:13)
3. Dull pain.
4. Is _____ thy companion, and the wife of thy covenant. (Mal. 2:14)
5. A very _____ day and a contentious woman are alike. (Prov. 27:15)
6. Choice marble.
7. None in the dialect.
8. The _____ of an enemy are deceitful. (Prov. 27:6)
9. Recorded proceedings.
10. Young salmon.
11. I give to eat of the _____ of life. (Rev. 2:7)
16. I will lay down my life for thy _____ . (John 13:37)
21. The man of _____ shall see thy name. (Mic. 6:9)
22. This sword is sharpened, and it is furbished, to give it into the hand of the _____ . (Ezek. 21:11)
23. River at the Balmoral Castle.
24. Professor of Divinity (initials).
25. Images of your mice that _____ the land. (1 Sam. 6:5)
26. _____ also the Jairite was a chief ruler about David. (2 Sam. 20:26)
27. Married woman's title.
28. John (Gaelic).
29. Jephunneh, and Pispah, and _____ . (1 Chron. 7:38)
30. Neither shall your vine cast _____ fruit before the time. (Mal. 3:11)
32. Uzziel, and Jerimoth, and _____ . (1 Chron. 7:7)
35. The angel of the LORD said to _____ the Tishbite, Arise, go up. (2 Kings 1:3)

36. Beloved, now are we the _____ of God. (1 John 3:2)
38. Then come and put your _____ in my shadow. (Judg. 9:15)
39. There came forth two she bears out of the wood, and _____ forty and two children. (2 Kings 2:24)
40. Type of collar, tie, or coat.
41. They smote him on the head with a _____ , and did spit upon him. (Mark 15:19)

42. Russian mountain range.
43. Slight in girth.
44. Distance (comb. form).
45. Manassas begat _____ . (Matt. 1:10)
48. High note.
49. Grandson of Rehoboam. (2 Chron. 14:1)

18

Across

1. Go to the _____, thou sluggard; consider her ways. (Prov. 6:6)
4. To whom the _____ of darkness is reserved for ever. (2 Peter 2:17)
8. _____ the flock of God which is among you. (1 Peter 5:2)
12. Card game.
13. _____ Domini.
14. Wave (French).
15. Jesus said unto them, _____ [2 words] the bread of life. (John 6:35)
16. Add to your faith virtue; and to virtue _____ . (2 Peter 1:5)
18. _____ shall come in the last days scoffers. (2 Peter 3:3)
20. Indiana Indian.
21. Persian weight.
22. Summer in Paris.
24. The _____ , which the LORD God had taken from man. (Gen. 2:22)
26. They shall proceed no _____ : for their folly shall be manifest. (2 Tim. 3:9)
30. Be not ye called _____ . (Matt. 23:8)
34. Thus _____ despised his birthright. (Gen. 25:34)
35. Tutelary Roman god.
37. Plumbing fittings.
38. Supernatural or inexplicable.
40. For the spirit of glory and of God _____ upon you. (1 Peter 4:14)
42. To doze.
44. Go, sell the _____ , and pay thy debt. (2 Kings 4:7)
45. Turkish chief.
48. Not any.
50. Bring your _____ under the yoke of the king of Babylon. (Jer. 27:12)
54. As the bird by _____ , as the swallow by flying. (Prov. 26:2)
57. Besought him that they might only touch the _____ of his garment. (Matt. 14:36)
58. To the sheltered side.
59. Fleshly lusts, which war against the _____ . (1 Peter 2:11)
60. Burmese premier (proper name).
61. The king's merchants received the linen _____ at a price. (1 Kings 10:28)
62. Being (Spanish).
63. That fadeth _____ away, reserved in heaven for you. (1 Peter 1:4)

Down

1. Past tense of "alight."
2. Saved _____ the eighth person. (2 Peter 2:5)
3. Large, scholarly volume.
4. Who _____ his angels spirits, and his ministers a flame of fire. (Heb. 1:7)
5. Set him on his own beast, and brought him to an _____ . (Luke 10:34)
6. Her Nazarites were purer than _____ . (Lam. 4:7)
7. Let us build us a city and a _____ . (Gen. 11:4)
8. Enemy.
9. The LORD shall judge the _____ of the earth. (1 Sam. 2:10)
10. If the iron be blunt, and he do not whet the _____ . (Eccles. 10:10)
11. Roe or hind.
17. Wild animal's den.
19. If it be not worthy, let your peace _____ to you. (Matt. 10:13)
23. Snakelike fish.
25. Gather them to the _____ of that great day of God Almighty. (Rev. 16:14)
26. Lord, are there _____ that be saved? (Luke 13:23)
27. _____ hospitality one to another without grudging. (1 Peter 4:9)
28. Siamese measure.
29. Scarce (German).
31. The _____ that is in the land of Assyria. (Isa. 7:18)
32. Wager.
33. Hebrew translation of "man."
36. Early American automobile.
39. Jutlander.
41. If therefore thine eye be _____ , thy whole body shall be full of light. (Matt. 6:22)

43. Cast in thy lot among us; let us all have one _____. (Prov. 1:14)
45. Ye shall receive a crown of glory that fadeth not _____. (1 Peter 5:4)
46. Festive occasion.
47. _____: and these were confederate with Abram. (Gen. 14:13)
49. Your adversary the devil, as a roaring _____. (1 Peter 5:8)

51. From _____, cities of Hadarezer. (1 Chron. 18:8)
52. Gambling game.
53. Obscene language.
55. The weaned child shall put his hand on the cockatrice' _____. (Isa. 11:8)
56. Hard-shelled seed.

19

Across

1. God walking in the garden in the _____ of the day. (Gen. 3:8)
5. David took an _____ , and played with his hand. (1 Sam. 16:23)
9. Then drew near unto him _____ the publicans and sinners. (Luke 15:1)
12. Air (comb. form).
13. Cake decorator.
14. Pasture.
15. He hath sent me to heal the _____ . (Luke 4:18)
18. Of his kingdom there shall be no _____ . (Luke 1:33)
19. Lo, these many _____ do I serve thee. (Luke 15:29)
20. Would not lift up so much as his eyes unto heaven, but _____ his breast. (Luke 18:13)
23. _____ not, neither by heaven, neither by the earth. (James 5:12)
25. _____ was tender eyed. (Gen. 29:17)
26. When they _____ it, they said, God forbid. (Luke 20:16)
27. They that heard them laid them _____ in their hearts. (Luke 1:66)
29. Do ye not therefore _____ , because ye know not the scriptures. (Mark 12:24)
30. We roar all like _____ , and mourn sore like doves. (Isa. 59:11)
31. Mineral spring or resort.
32. _____ , being delivered out of the hand of our enemies, might serve him. (Luke 1:74)
33. Soviet mountain range.
34. The wise men.
35. Sleighs.
36. Active physical or mental strength.
37. Central part of a Roman amphitheater.
39. The fowls of the _____ lodged in the branches of it. (Luke 13:19)
40. _____ , [2 words] which also was the traitor. (Luke 6:16)
46. Third king of Judah.
47. Jogging pace.
48. Wine measure (Trieste).
49. He _____ before, and climbed up into a sycomore tree. (Luke 19:4)
50. Who can forgive _____ , but God alone? (Luke 5:21)
51. Sendeth _____ on the just and on the unjust. (Matt. 5:45)

Down

1. The fourth part of a _____ of dove's dung for five pieces of silver. (2 Kings 6:25)
2. Over (poetic).
3. Gold (Spanish).
4. Where it _____ him best: thou shalt not oppress him. (Deut. 23:16)
5. Naphtali is a _____ let loose. (Gen. 49:21)
6. Alas (German).
7. Befuddled (Scottish).
8. Gold vials full of odours, which are the _____ of saints. (Rev. 5:8)
9. Zacharias, which perished between the _____ and the temple. (Luke 11:51)
10. A cunning glance.
11. The angel which redeemed me from all evil, bless the _____ . (Gen. 48:16)
16. Direction from Bethlehem to Philadelphia.
17. Have ye not _____ so much as this, what David did? (Luke 6:3)
20. The tower in Siloam fell, and _____ them. (Luke 13:4)
21. Nothing more than what is specified.
22. All that handle the _____ , the mariners. (Ezek. 27:29)
23. Written within and on the backside, sealed with seven _____ . (Rev. 5:1)
24. Ye shall hear of _____ and commotions. (Luke 21:9)
26. The Son of man hath not where to lay his _____ . (Luke 9:58)
27. To ascend.
28. A _____ of turtledoves, or two young pigeons. (Luke 2:24)
30. Beholding the things which were done, smote their _____ . (Luke 23:48)
31. If a man is lazy, the rafters _____ . (Eccles. 10:18, NIV)
33. Forearm bone.

34. Like a man who looks at his face in a
_____ . (James 1:23, NIV)
35. Two-seated enclosed vehicle.
36. By way of.
37. Slightly open.
38. East Indian deer genus.
39. Who can utter the mighty _____ of
the LORD? (Ps. 106:2)
41. Sons of Bela: Ezbon, and Uzzi, and
Uzziel, and Jerimoth, and _____ .
(1 Chron. 7:7)

42. He shall be great, and shall be called
the _____ of the Highest. (Luke 1:32)
43. _____ the son of Ikkesh the Tekoite.
(2 Sam. 23:26)
44. She called his name Ben-_____ : but
his father called him Benjamin. (Gen.
35:18)
45. Were there not _____ cleansed?
(Luke 17:17)

20

Across

1. Turkish river.
5. Make up the hedge, and stand in the _____ before me. (Ezek. 22:30)
8. Judas begat Phares and _____ . (Matt. 1:3)
12. When Jesus saw it, he was _____ displeased. (Mark 10:14)
13. Coarse Near East garment.
14. Thou hast been in _____ the garden of God. (Ezek. 28:13)
15. In the visions of _____ the seer. (2 Chron. 9:29)
16. Cause their rivers to _____ like oil, saith the Lord GOD. (Ezek. 32:14)
17. Name derived from "Elizabeth."
18. Fifty-fifth book of the Bible (2 words).
21. And upon the great _____ of his right foot. (Lev. 14:14)
22. I will _____ off the multitude of No. (Ezek. 30:15)
23. As a _____ doth gather her brood under her wings. (Luke 13:34)
26. An abstract being.
28. The Philistines have _____ by revenge. (Ezek. 25:15)
32. Mattathias, which was the son of _____ . (Luke 3:25)
34. Behold, there _____ women weeping for Tammuz. (Ezek. 8:14)
36. Until the day dawn, and the day _____ arise in your hearts. (2 Peter 1:19)
37. Neither give place to the _____ . (Eph. 4:27)
39. To _____ , Jerusalem, and the cities of Judah. (Jer. 25:18)
41. Noun suffix meaning "state of."
42. Most recent period subdivision (comb. form).
44. Son of _____ , eat that thou findest. (Ezek. 3:1)
46. Old Testament book celebrating love (3 words).
53. _____ the Ahohite. (1 Chron. 11:29)
54. And looking back, is _____ for the kingdom of God. (Luke 9:62)

55. Jealousy is the _____ of a man. (Prov. 6:34)
56. I will give free _____ to my complaint and speak out. (Job 10:1, NIV)
57. Anglo-Saxon letter.
58. I will multiply the fruit of the _____ . (Ezek. 36:30)
59. Thou art unto them as a very lovely _____ . (Ezek. 33:32)
60. King (Spanish).
61. Take _____ that no man deceive you. (Matt. 24:4)

Down

1. Friends (French).
2. Though I be _____ in speech, yet not in knowledge. (2 Cor. 11:6)
3. Types of electrical current (2).
4. _____ at her, spare no arrows. (Jer. 50:14)
5. Thou that dwellest in the _____ . (Song of Sol. 8:13)
6. To border upon.
7. There is _____ , not joy, upon the mountains. (Ezek. 7:7, NIV)
8. Simon called _____ . (Luke 6:15)
9. Mine entrance.
10. Hebrew letter.
11. Guatemalan fruit.
19. As the days of _____ were, so shall also the coming of the Son of man be. (Matt. 24:37)
20. He put _____ on my eyes, the man replied. (John 9:15, NIV)
23. I _____ pity for mine holy name. (Ezek. 36:21)
24. Uncle (Scottish).
25. November (abbrev.).
27. The heavens were opened, and I _____ visions of God. (Ezek. 1:1)
29. And _____ the sacrifices of the dead. (Ps. 106:28)
30. Malayan ape.
31. Let us search and _____ our ways, and turn again to the LORD. (Lam. 3:40)
33. Break forth into _____ , ye mountains, O forest. (Isa. 44:23)

Grid numbers: 1 2 3 4 | 5 6 7 | 8 9 10 11 / 12 13 14 / 15 16 17 / 18 19 20 / 21 22 / 23 24 25 26 27 28 29 30 31 / 32 33 34 35 36 / 37 38 39 40 41 / 42 43 44 45 / 46 47 48 49 50 51 52 / 53 54 55 / 56 57 58 / 59 60 61

35. Our brother _____ is set at liberty. (Heb. 13:23)
38. Pope's name.
40. Palm fiber.
43. Ye shall _____ the holy oblation foursquare. (Ezek. 48:20)
45. A whirlwind came out of the _____, a great cloud. (Ezek. 1:4)
46. Wherefore, _____, be of good cheer. (Acts 27:25)

47. Pertaining to oil (comb. form).
48. He went into a city called _____. (Luke 7:11)
49. Clothed with linen, with a writer's inkhorn by his _____ . (Ezek. 9:2)
50. I liken you, my darling, to a _____. (Song of Sol. 1:9, NIV)
51. S-shaped molding.
52. Have I _____ of mad men? (1 Sam. 21:15)

43

21

Across

1. He shall suck the poison of _____. (Job 20:16)
5. Issachar is a strong _____ crouching down between two burdens. (Gen. 49:14)
8. Large bundle of goods.
12. My ears have heard the _____ of my wicked foes. (Ps. 92:11, NIV)
13. He lieth in wait secretly as a lion in his _____. (Ps. 10:9)
14. The man spake unto Ithiel, even unto Ithiel and _____. (Prov. 30:1)
15. Air (comb. form).
16. Deoxyribonucleic acid.
17. Whosoever shall say to his brother _____ shall be in danger. (Matt. 5:22)
18. Bar or spy.
20. The Lord hath _____ under foot all my mighty men. (Lam. 1:15)
22. My skin hath he made old; he hath _____ my bones. (Lam. 3:4)
25. Direction from Nazareth to the Sea of Galilee.
26. Expressions of surprise.
27. Faint for hunger in the _____ of every street. (Lam. 2:19)
29. Neither say thou before the _____, that it was an error. (Eccles. 5:6)
33. To pass through slowly.
35. Let us eat and drink, for tomorrow we shall _____. (Isa. 22:13)
37. Withered or scorched.
38. _____, that was overthrown as in a moment. (Lam. 4:6)
40. Ostrich-like bird.
42. Direction from Joppa to Nazareth.
43. In the first chariot were _____ horses. (Zech. 6:2)
45. Strikes.
47. Persecute and _____ them in anger from under the heavens. (Lam. 3:66)
51. Of Zebaim, the children of _____. (Ezra 2:57)
52. I saw in a vision, and I was by the river of _____. (Dan. 8:2)
53. _____, and pay unto the LORD your God. (Ps. 76:11)
55. Salted.
58. North Atlantic Treaty Organization (abbrev.).
59. To survive with great effort.
60. The priests had burned incense, from _____ to Beer-sheba. (2 Kings 23:8)
61. Federal agents.
62. He hath bent his bow, and _____ me as a mark. (Lam. 3:12)
63. _____ the father of the Edomites. (Gen. 36:9)

Down

1. Jephunneh, and Pispah, and _____. (1 Chron. 7:38)
2. Wooden pail.
3. The LORD hath _____ to destroy the wall of the daughter of Zion. (Lam. 2:8)
4. The _____ in heaven knoweth her appointed times. (Jer. 8:7)
5. I will _____ to your yoke. (1 Kings 12:11)
6. From above hath he _____ fire into my bones. (Lam. 1:13)
7. Fear and a _____ is come upon us. (Lam. 3:47)
8. Seen for thee false _____ and causes of banishment. (Lam. 2:14)
9. Academic (abbrev.).
10. Thou shalt put it on a blue _____. (Exod. 28:37)
11. Enthusiasm.
19. Our eyes as _____ failed for our vain help. (Lam. 4:17)
21. Cape Horn Indian.
22. Fish or voice.
23. Current or flow (comb. form).
24. Dwelt in the land of _____, east of Eden. (Gen. 4:16)
28. A filled pastry shell.
30. Her king and her princes are among the _____. (Lam. 2:9)
31. White-tailed sea eagle.
32. Punish the men that are settled on their _____. (Zeph. 1:12)
34. The LORD is my _____, saith my soul. (Lam. 3:24)
36. Prussian spa town.
39. Sea (French).

1	2	3	4		5	6	7		8	9	10	11
12					13				14			
15					16				17			
	18		19		20		21					
22	23				24		25					
26				27		28		29		30	31	32
33			34		35		36		37			
38				39		40		41		42		
			43		44		45		46			
47	48	49			50			51				
52				53		54		55			56	57
58				59				60				
61				62				63				

41. Hindu figure of splendor.
44. Shall be on the mountains like _____ of the valleys. (Ezek. 7:16)
46. The molten _____ , and a teacher of lies. (Hab. 2:18)
47. The fourth part of a cab of dove's _____ . (2 Kings 6:25)
48. I will break the bow of _____ . (Jer. 49:35)

49. To glut.
50. It's good for a man that he bear the _____ in his youth. (Lam. 3:27)
54. They are _____ with the showers of the mountains. (Job 24:8)
56. Arab cloak.
57. Twenty-second Hebrew letter

45

22

Across

1. Rounded projection.
5. Whenever David attacked an _____ _, he did not leave a man or woman alive. (1 Sam. 27:9, NIV)
9. Love worketh no _____ to his neighbor. (Rom. 13:10)
12. Voyaging, especially by water.
13. College official.
14. Gods (Latin).
15. Halfpennies.
16. Him who hath called you out of _____ . (1 Peter 2:9)
18. Silvanus, a faithful _____ unto you. (1 Peter 5:12)
20. That at the _____ the shadow of Peter passing by might overshadow some. (Acts 5:15)
21. Put the ball on the stand.
22. If any man suffer as a Christian, _____ him not be ashamed. (1 Peter 4:16)
23. Capital city of the Nabataeans.
25. Egyptian god of music and revelry.
26. Four-year science degrees.
29. Doth God take care for _____ ? (1 Cor. 9:9)
30. Why is thy spirit so _____, that thou eatest no bread? (1 Kings 21:5)
31. Wild plum.
32. Ye have _____ thousand instructors in Christ. (1 Cor. 4:15)
33. Ye are grown _____ as the heifer at grass, and bellow as bulls. (Jer. 50:11)
34. They cast four anchors out of the _____ . (Acts 27:29)
35. How doth the city _____ solitary, that was full of people! (Lam. 1:1)
36. Depart from me, ye _____ , into everlasting fire. (Matt. 25:41)
37. Manoah knew not that he was an _____ of the LORD. (Judg. 13:16)
40. _____ was a man subject to like passions as we are. (James 5:17)
41. Which _____ were disobedient, when once the longsuffering of God waited. (1 Peter 3:20)
43. Unless (Latin).

46. The serpent beguiled _____ through his subtilty. (2 Cor. 11:3)
47. Of plaiting the _____ , and of wearing gold. (1 Peter 3:3)
48. Ye blind guides, which strain at a _____ . (Matt. 23:24)
49. Centurions, and _____ down unto them. (Acts 21:32)
50. Egg's yellow.
51. The partridge sitteth on _____ . (Jer. 17:11)

Down

1. As of a _____ without blemish and without spot. (1 Peter 1:19)
2. Sandy glacial ridge.
3. To his abundant mercy hath _____ us again. (1 Peter 1:3)
4. Aram, the king of Moab from the _____ mountains. (Num. 23:7, NIV)
5. It was _____ because of transgressions, till the seed should come. (Gal. 3:19)
6. Wilt thou _____ it up in three days? (John 2:20)
7. Smote a servant of the high priest, and cut off his _____ . (Mark 14:47)
8. Instantly the man's feet and _____ became strong. (Acts 3:7, NIV)
9. Is that your own _____ , Jesus asked. (John 18:34, NIV)
10. The more abundantly I love you, the _____ I be loved. (2 Cor. 12:15)
11. _____ my tears on your scroll. (Ps. 56:8, NIV)
17. As a wild bull in a _____ ; they are full of fury. (Isa. 51:20)
19. Chief Babylonian deity.
22. Lest ye also, being _____ away with the error. (2 Peter 3:17)
23. I see a seething _____ . (Jer. 1:13)
24. River in Devon.
25. The hoopoe and the _____ . (Lev. 11:19, NIV)
26. Or railing for railing; but contrariwise _____ . (1 Peter 3:9)
27. The LORD hath chastened me _____ . (Ps. 118:18)

28. Make merry, and shall _____ gifts one to another. (Rev. 11:10)
30. Lot _____ in the gate of Sodom. (Gen. 19:1)
31. Think it not _____ concerning the fiery trail. (1 Peter 4:12)
33. Not for _____ lucre, but of a ready mind. (1 Peter 5:2)
34. Chinese dynasty.
35. He that will love life, and _____ good days. (1 Peter 3:10)
36. When the town _____ had appeased the people. (Acts 19:35)
37. Asher (KJV).
38. Type of star.
39. Federal agents.
40. French writer Zola.
42. Samoan wattlebird.
44. If a man is lazy, the rafters _____ . (Eccles. 10:18, NIV)
45. That which groweth of _____ own accord of thy harvest. (Lev. 25:5)

23

Across

1. Apparel.
5. Arise, take up thy _____ . (Matt. 9:6)
8. First _____ out the beam out of thine own eye. (Matt. 7:5)
12. Mountain in Crete.
13. All things _____ ready: come unto the marriage. (Matt. 22:4)
14. The man who was healed had no _____ who it was. (John 5:13, NIV)
15. Without all contradiction the _____ is blessed of the better. (Heb. 7:7)
16. December (abbrev.).
17. Bring forth therefore fruits _____ for repentance. (Matt. 3:8)
18. Come ye yourselves apart into a desert place, and rest _____ . (Mark 6:31)
20. Everyone who joins in the work, and _____ at it. (1 Cor. 16:16, NIV)
22. Blessed are they which _____ hunger and thirst. (Matt. 5:6)
23. He that sat on him had a _____ of balances in his hand. (Rev. 6:5)
24. The king arose, and _____ his garments, and lay on the earth. (2 Sam. 13:31)
27. As many as ye shall find, bid to the _____ . (Matt. 22:9)
31. _____ the son of Ikkesh the Tekoite. (2 Sam. 23:26)
32. A feast of _____ on the lees. (Isa. 25:6)
33. A tenth of a sen.
34. Thy _____ delight my soul. (Ps. 94:19)
36. With all thy heart, and with all thy soul, and with all thy _____ . (Matt. 22:37)
37. Historical periods.
38. _____ , every one that thirsteth, come ye to the waters. (Isa. 55:1)
39. Large-eared African fox.
42. Wherein was the golden pot that had manna, and _____ rod that budded. (Heb. 9:4)
46. Herring.
47. Cast in thy _____ among us; let us all have one purse. (Prov. 1:14)
49. He wrote also letters to _____ on the LORD God of Israel. (2 Chron. 32:17)
50. The people shall be as the burnings of _____ . (Isa. 33:12)
51. Ye do _____ , not knowing the scriptures. (Matt. 22:29)
52. German monarch.
53. Be not, as the hypocrites, of _____ [2 words] countenance. (Matt. 6:16)
54. The pure in heart: for they shall _____ God. (Matt. 5:8)
55. Who _____ their tongue like a sword. (Ps. 64:3)

Down

1. Large venomous lizard.
2. Jacob shall be in the midst of many people as _____ [2 words] from the LORD. (Mic. 5:7)
3. The heart also of the _____ shall understand knowledge. (Isa. 32:4)
4. I have gained _____ them five talents more. (Matt. 25:20)
5. He _____ them not beware of the leaven of bread. (Matt. 16:12)
6. Previously (poetic).
7. The time is coming, _____ the Lord, when I will make a new covenant. (Heb. 8:8, NIV)
8. Ancient North European tribe.
9. Exactly (Latin).
10. O thou _____ , go, flee thee away. (Amos 7:12)
11. Makes lace.
19. There shall ye see him: _____ , I have told you. (Matt. 28:7)
21. Ventilates.
23. As the deer _____ for streams of water. (Ps. 42:1, NIV)
24. Muscle spasm.
25. Nigerian native.
26. Barachel the Buzite, of the kindred of _____ . (Job 32:2)
27. Ye seek me, not because ye saw the _____ , but because ye did eat. (John 6:26)
28. Biblical lion.
29. The _____ shall take him by the heel. (Job 18:9)

30. He that endureth to the _____ shall be saved. (Matt. 10:22)
32. He _____ cursing as his garment. (Ps. 109:18, NIV)
35. And he _____ it, and gathered out the stones thereof. (Isa. 5:2)
36. Which to day is, and to _____ is cast into the oven. (Matt. 6:30)
38. He saith among the trumpets, _____ . (Job 39:25)
39. F. D. R.'s dog or song refrain.
40. The iniquity of _____ house shall not be purged. (1 Sam. 3:14)
41. Thread (comb. form).
42. Hearth (French).
43. He promised with an _____ to give her whatsoever she would ask. (Matt. 14:7)
44. Night (var.).
45. Long, narrow opening or groove.
48. And copper is smelted from _____ . (Job 28:2, NIV)

24

Across

1. Jewish teachers.
5. Then shall he kill the _____ of the sin offering. (Lev. 16:15)
9. _____ is worthy to open the book? (Rev. 5:2)
12. Kemuel the father of _____. (Gen. 22:21)
13. You will be protected from the _____ of the tongue. (Job 5:21, NIV)
14. Stones to cast at him, but Jesus _____ himself. (John 8:59)
15. _____ [3 words] all ye Gentiles, and laud him. (Rom. 15:11)
18. Afternoon socials.
19. It shall stop the _____ of the passengers. (Ezek. 39:11)
20. The _____ image, and a teacher of lies. (Hab. 2:18)
23. Eight's prefix.
24. Double-reeded woodwinds.
25. _____ no man any thing, but to love one another. (Rom. 13:8)
26. Uncle (Scottish).
29. Sea swallow.
30. To be ill.
31. John (Welsh).
32. Wherewith the _____ number of them is to be redeemed. (Num. 3:48)
33. _____ Abner.
34. They cast four anchors out of the _____, and waited for day. (Acts 27:29)
35. A certain _____ beheld him as he sat by the fire. (Luke 22:56)
37. Turn from thy _____ wrath, and repent of this evil. (Exod. 32:12)
38. Caucasion Gentile.
40. Click beetle.
41. _____, and peace, and joy in the Holy Ghost. (Rom. 14:17)
46. Conceit.

47. Thou saidst, I shall be a lady for _____. (Isa. 47:7)
48. _____ for the day! for the day of the LORD is at hand. (Joel 1:15)
49. Be not, as the hypocrites, of a _____ countenance. (Matt. 6:16)
50. Mary the mother of James the _____ and of Joses. (Mark 15:40)
51. Fuzz.

Down

1. Quick, sharp blow.
2. They do away _____ in their heart. (Heb. 3:10)
3. Bleat.
4. Ephraim is _____, their root is dried up. (Hos. 9:16)
5. Let her _____ even among the sheaves. (Ruth 2:15)
6. Cereal grains.
7. He planteth an _____, and the rain doth nourish it. (Isa. 44:14)
8. The LORD scattered them abroad from _____ upon the face of all the earth. (Gen. 11:8).
9. _____ heareth of it, both his ears shall tingle. (2 Kings 21:12)
10. The labourer is worthy of his _____. (Luke 10:7)
11. Ratio expressing probability.
16. Your Father, who _____ what is done in secret. (Matt. 6:4, NIV)
17. And the _____ fell upon Jonah. (Jonah 1:7)
20. Musical movement.
21. _____ begat Jesse, and Jesse begat David. (Ruth 4:22)
22. O _____ [3 words], I cried unto thee, and thou hast healed me. (Ps. 30:2)
23. I am like an _____ of the desert. (Ps. 102:6)

25. Give us of your _____ ; for our lamps are gone out. (Matt. 25:8)
27. Chagall.
28. Nine (comb. form).
30. You sent me _____ again and again when I was in need. (Phil. 4:16, NIV).
31. Thou hast the words of _____ life. (John 6:68)
33. Smite the _____ of the door, that the posts may shake. (Amos 9:1)
34. _____ , what must I do to be saved? (Acts 16:30)

36. Exclamation of wonder.
37. One more than threes.
38. Greek god of war.
39. Scotch pine.
40. I say to my servant, Do this, and he _____ it. (Luke 7:8, NIV)
42. Adam called his wife's name _____ . (Gen. 3:20)
43. _____ thought she had been drunken. (1 Sam. 1:13)
44. Santo (Spanish contraction).
45. Fastest passenger plane.

25

Across

1. Deoxyribonucleic acid (abbrev.).
4. When he saw him, straightway the spirit _____ him. (Mark 9:20)
8. By faith _____ offered unto God a more excellent sacrifice. (Heb. 11:4)
12. _____ not the poor, because he is poor. (Prov. 22:22)
13. Ireland.
14. Muse of history.
15. Indian mulberry.
16. Howl, ye _____ of the altar; come, lie all night in sackcloth. (Joel 1:13)
18. Where the lion, even the old lion, walked, and the lion's _____ . (Nah. 2:11)
20. Din.
21. Hebrew letter.
24. We (Latin).
25. Dug out.
29. He had _____ hundred chariots of iron. (Judg. 4:3)
32. Exclamation of contact.
33. Barnabas, and _____ , chief men among the brethren. (Acts 15:22)
35. Let them not feed, _____ drink water. (Jonah 3:7)
36. After the most straitest _____ of our religion I lived a Pharisee. (Acts 26:5)
38. Thy brother in the day that he became a _____ . (Obad. 12)
40. Pronoun (Italian).
42. Slender bristle.
43. Nuts of an oak.
46. In those days will _____ [2 words] out my spirit. (Joel 2:29)
50. Awake, ye _____ , and weep. (Joel 1:5)
53. Bitter beer.
54. An easterner or a dandy.

55. In her mouth was an olive_____ pluckt off. (Gen. 8:11)
56. To treat hides.
57. Soviet Union.
58. Man's name.
59. The Valley of Jehoshaphat, for there I will _____ to judge. (Joel 3:12, NIV)

Down

1. Prepare war, wake up the mighty men, let all the men of war _____ near. (Joel 3:9)
2. This is as the waters of _____ unto me. (Isa. 54:9)
3. Believe ye that I am _____ to do this? (Matt. 9:28)
4. Carried into your _____ my goodly pleasant things. (Joel 3:5)
5. Biblical lion.
6. Tenth of a sen.
7. Grape skin pigment.
8. Moses . . . was powerful in speech and _____ . (Acts 7:22, NIV)
9. Repent, and leave a _____ behind. (Joel 2:14)
10. Ireland.
11. I have suffered the _____ of all things, and do count them but dung. (Phil. 3:8)
17. The word of the LORD came to Joel the _____ of Pethuel. (Joel 1:1)
19. Gypsy word.
22. The iniquity of _____ house shall not be purged with sacrifice. (1 Sam. 3:14)
23. Compressed wool fabrics.
25. Distress signal.
26. Color by perception.
27. A day _____ [2 words] and of thick darkness. (Joel 2:2)

1	2	3	■	4	5	6	7	■	8	9	10	11
12			■	13				■	14			
15			■	16			■	17				
18			19		■	■	20					
■	■	21		■	22	23	■	24			■	■
25	26	27					28	■	29		30	31
32			33			■	34		35			
36		37	■	38			■	39				
■	40		41		42			■	■	■	■	■
43	44			■	45		■	46		47	48	49
50				51	52	■	■	53				
54			■	55			■	56				
57			■	58			■	59				

28. None is so fierce that _____ stir him up. (Job 41:10)
30. Until the day that _____ entered into the ark. (Luke 17:27)
31. The spirit of whoredoms hath caused them to _____ . (Hos. 4:12)
34. In the day of the wrath of the LORD: they shall not _____ their souls. (Ezek. 7:19)
37. One which rotates.
39. Siesta.
41. I wrote them with _____ in the book. (Jer. 36:18)
43. Babylonian storm deity.
44. Shank.
45. And she became a pillar of _____ . (Gen. 19:26)
47. Breakfast grains.
48. I heard a man's voice between the banks of _____ . (Dan. 8:16)
49. The cloud is not _____ under them. (Job 26:8)
51. Early automobile.
52. _____ shall be a serpent by the way, an adder in the path. (Gen. 49:17)

26

Across

1. Ye shall have a _____, as in the night. (Isa. 30:29)
5. The trees of the LORD are full of _____. (Ps. 104:16)
8. The children of Zibeon; both _____, and Anah. (Gen. 36:24)
12. Hebrew month.
13. Arab cloak.
14. Festival.
15. _____ is waxed feeble. (Jer. 49:24)
17. Steel-wedged tool.
18. To seduce, if it were possible, even the _____. (Mark 13:22)
19. The prayer of faith shall save the sick, and _____ [2 words] shall raise him up. (James 5:15)
21. Rise, Peter; kill, and _____. (Acts 10:13)
23. What Eve was made of (2 words).
24. Afternoon social.
27. I have not sent these prophets, yet they _____. (Jer. 23:21)
29. School (French).
32. American holly.
34. Behind him a _____ caught in a thicket by his horns. (Gen. 22:13)
36. He moveth his _____ like a cedar. (Job 40:17)
37. Esaias saith, There shall be a root of _____. (Rom. 15:12)
39. He saith, _____. And when he was come into the house, Jesus prevented him. (Matt. 17:25)
41. Man's name.
42. Historical time periods.
44. Sem, which was the son of _____. (Luke 3:36)
46. Thine elder sister is _____. (Ezek. 16:46)
49. Jonathan David's _____ was a counsellor, a wise man, and a scribe. (1 Chron. 27:32)
53. Priest (French).
54. _____ shall see it, and fear. (Zech. 9:5)
56. A golden _____ and a pomegranate. (Exod. 28:34)
57. We sailed to the _____ of Crete. (Acts 27:7, NIV)
58. Walk not as other Gentiles walk, in the vanity of their _____. (Eph. 4:17)
59. Woman's name.
60. Hockey great.
61. Be not entangled again with the _____ of bondage. (Gal. 5:1)

Down

1. Hebrew letter.
2. Ancient Scandinavian estate.
3. His _____ shall be in their foreheads. (Rev. 22:4)
4. Noah found _____ in the eyes of the LORD. (Gen. 6:8)
5. Pouch.
6. Border on.
7. Russian name.
8. At that time I will undo all that _____ thee. (Zeph. 3:19)
9. _____ the son of Nebat, an Ephrathite of Zereda, Solomon's servant. (1 Kings 11:26)
10. One who acts (comb. form).
11. Take _____ to the ministry which thou hast received in the Lord. (Col. 4:17)
16. Your images, the _____ of your god, which ye made to yourselves. (Amos 5:26)
20. Before (poetic).
22. The Valley of Siddim was full of _____ pits. (Gen. 14:10, NIV)
24. Agra mausoleum.
25. Direction from Jerusalem to Bethany.

54

26. I will praise the LORD with my whole heart, in the _____ of the upright. (Ps. 111:1)
28. _____, I had not known sin, but by the law. (Rom. 7:7)
30. _____ not one to another. (Col. 3:9)
31. Building wing.
33. The LORD had done unto Pharaoh and to the Egyptians for _____ sake. (Exod. 18:8)
35. Philosophy and vain deceit, after the tradition of _____ . (Col. 2:8)
38. Hear this, ye old men, and give _____ . (Joel 1:2)

40. Muslim marketplace.
43. Saliva (comb. form).
45. A friend of the world is the _____ of God. (James 4:4)
46. Sheba (Latin).
47. They shall surely ask counsel at _____ . (2 Sam. 20:18)
48. Anna, a prophetess, the daughter of Phanuel, of the tribe of _____ . (Luke 2:36)
50. Muse of history.
51. Black-faced sheep.
52. Therefore (Spanish).
55. Cast out the bondwoman and _____ son. (Gal. 4:30)

27

Across

1. A poor man hears no _____ . (Prov. 13:8, NIV)
7. Minute quantities.
13. One that _____ well his own house, having his children in subjection. (1 Tim. 3:4)
14. Capital of Cuba.
15. The letter *m*.
16. Understanding neither what they say, _____ whereof they affirm. (1 Tim. 1:7)
17. The serpent beguiled _____ through his subtilty. (2 Cor. 11:3)
18. Audiovisual (abbrev.).
19. Graduate degree.
21. Civil War general.
23. His mother's name also was _____ , the daughter of Zachariah. (2 Kings 18:2)
24. Russian woman's name.
26. Direction from Jerusalem to Jericho.
27. Capital of Norway.
28. The earth _____ like a drunkard. (Isa. 24:20, NIV)
30. Rabbi, we know that thou art a _____ come from God. (John 3:2)
32. A three-base hit. (2 words)
34. _____-Christian ethic (2 words).
37. Rebekah had a brother, and his name was _____ . (Gen. 24:29)
41. Behold, I _____ you forth as sheep in the midst of wolves. (Matt. 10:16)
42. School (abbrev.).
44. Little girl (Spanish).
45. Son of Bela.
46. Eli, the LORD's priest in Shiloh, wearing an _____ . (1 Sam. 14:3)
48. Military decoration.
49. _____ all things without murmurings and disputings. (Phil. 2:14)
50. Large primate.
51. The LORD that delivered me out of the _____ of the lion. (1 Sam. 17:37)
53. _____ have many members in one body. (Rom. 12:4)
54. Vomit-inducing medicine.
56. One which wipes out.
58. Go at once and _____ the animals for your families. (Exod. 12:21, NIV)
59. Interior decoratings.

Down

1. Vibration.
2. The _____ shall see this, and be glad. (Ps. 69:32)
3. Author Stevenson's initials.
4. Yet (poetic).
5. Smallest particle of matter.
6. There are _____ that bear record in heaven. (1 John 5:7)
7. The Spirit searcheth all things, yea, _____ [2 words] things of God. (1 Cor. 2:10)
8. Speak incoherently.
9. Hail.
10. Calcium (abbrev.).
11. His heart desires, but God does not _____ him to enjoy them. (Eccles. 6:2, NIV)
12. See, your _____ comes! See, his reward is with him. (Isa. 62:11, NIV)
20. He is of _____ , ask him. (John 9:23)
22. Nicolas a proselyte of _____ . (Acts 6:5)
23. He planteth an _____ , and the rain doth nourish it. (Isa. 44:14)
25. Star of "Shane" (1913–1964).
27. Large body of water.
29. Musical rest.
31. For _____ have sinned, and come short of the glory of God. (Rom. 3:23)
33. Though the LORD be high, yet hath he _____ unto the lowly. (Ps. 138:6)
34. Digressions.
35. Compiler of the Latin Vulgate.
36. Single (comb. form).
38. Receive him not into your house, neither _____ him God speed. (2 John 10)
39. Be ready always to give an _____ to every man that asketh you a reason of the hope that is in you. (1 Peter 3:15)
40. Bestowers of appellations.
43. This they did, not as we _____ , but first gave their own selves to the Lord. (2 Cor. 8:5)

46. Heroic poem.
47. _____ any of you, having a matter against another, go to law? (1 Cor. 6:1)
50. I took the little book out of the angel's hand, and _____ it up. (Rev. 10:10)
52. American airwoman.
55. God (Hebrew).
57. As ye have therefore received Christ Jesus the Lord, _____ walk ye in him. (Col. 2:6)

28

Across

1. Law (French).
4. Dinah, the daughter of _____ . (Gen. 34:1)
8. Every branch in me _____ beareth not fruit he taketh away. (John 15:2)
12. Whose _____ shall be according to their works. (2 Cor. 11:15)
13. Medieval lyric.
14. Booz begat Obed of _____ . (Matt. 1:5)
15. High card.
16. Boggy wasteland.
17. Shammah the son of _____ the Hararite. (2 Sam. 23:11)
18. Grace be to you and _____ from God the Father. (Gal. 1:3)
20. They will _____ out of his kingdom everything that causes sin. (Matt. 13:41, NIV)
22. Bear ye _____ another's burdens. (Gal. 6:2)
24. Faucet.
28. Sounded like a hog.
32. Piece of music for study.
33. German name meaning "Fame-Wolf."
34. Uncover thy locks, make bare the _____ . (Isa. 47:2)
36. He esteemeth _____ as straw. (Job 41:27)
37. With speed.
39. In all my _____ they shall find none iniquity in me. (Hos. 12:8)
41. As the eyes of a _____ unto the hand of her mistress. (Ps. 123:2)
43. Is this house, which is called by my name, become a _____ of robbers? (Jer. 7:11)
44. Gaal the son of _____ . (Judg. 9:28)
46. Happy am I, for the daughters will call me blessed: and she called his name _____ . (Gen. 30:13)
50. The children of Dishan are these; Uz, and _____ . (Gen. 36:28)
53. He that is now called a Prophet was beforetime called a _____ . (1 Sam. 9:9)
55. Who built _____ , and Lod, with the towns thereof. (1 Chron. 8:12)

56. Circular plate.
57. The thoughts of the diligent _____ only to plenteousness. (Prov. 21:5)
58. Mythical bird.
59. Bishop's seat.
60. Hope (Latin).
61. If any of you lack wisdom, let him _____ of God. (James 1:5)

Down

1. Why _____ ye, ye high hills? (Ps. 68:16)
2. Forgive, I pray thee, my sin only this _____ . (Exod. 10:17)
3. He had no _____ that what the angel was doing was really happening. (Acts 12:9, NIV)
4. They will _____ thee, saying, Ah lord! (Jer. 34:5)
5. Eastern longitudinal abbreviation.
6. A white horse, and he that sat on him had _____ [2 words]. (Rev. 6:2)
7. Long-eared rabbits.
8. Hold the _____ which ye have been taught. (2 Thess. 2:15)
9. They are drenched by mountain rains and _____ the rocks for lack of shelter. (Job 24:8, NIV)
10. I _____ no pleasant bread. (Dan. 10:3)
11. We are not of _____ night, nor of darkness. (1 Thess. 5:5)
19. We have _____ in the Lord touching you. (2 Thess. 3:4)
21. Gall (Hungarian).
23. Snake-like fish.
25. Spiritual teacher.
26. By this time there is a bad _____ , for he has been there four days. (John 11:39, NIV)
27. Captains over _____ , and officers among your tribes. (Deut. 1:15)
28. Unit of weight.
29. Italian city.
30. I saw in a vision, and I was by the river of _____ . (Dan. 8:2)
31. Of the (Spanish).
35. Blessed be he that enlargeth _____ . (Deut. 33:20)

38. Bird beak.
40. Shaved off the one half of their ______. (2 Sam. 10:4)
42. Birds of the air have ______. (Luke 9:58)
45. Woe unto them that seek ______ to hide their counsel from the LORD. (Isa. 29:15)
47. Israeli dance.
48. ______, which was the son of Seth. (Luke 3:38)
49. Hide it there in a hole of the ______. (Jer. 13:4)
50. Woman's name.
51. Dash their children, and ______ up their women. (2 Kings 8:12)
52. A wild ______ alone by himself. (Hos. 8:9)
54. Direction from Jerusalem to Cyprus.

29

Across

1. The _____ of my dispersed, shall bring mine offering. (Zeph. 3:10)
9. By one _____ offence death reigned. (Rom. 5:17)
13. Treat . . . younger women as sisters, with _____ purity. (1 Tim. 5:2)
14. The canals will _____ a stench. (Isa. 19:6, ASV).
15. Whatsoever ye do in word or _____ . (Col. 3:17)
16. Could not be eaten, they were so _____ . (Jer. 24:2)
17. Seeing a _____ fig tree by the road, He came to it. (Matt. 21:19, ASV)
18. Seeing that ye have put off the _____ man with his deeds. (Col. 3:9)
19. Jacob sojourned in the land of _____ . (Ps. 105:23)
20. _____ , Go, take unto thee a wife of whoredoms. (Hos. 1:2)
21. To feel ill.
22. Ye have made it a _____ of thieves. (Mark 11:17)
23. Thallium (abbrev.).
24. God shall _____ thee, thou whited wall. (Acts 23:3)
27. That we may present every _____ perfect in Christ Jesus. (Col. 1:28)
28. Gods (Latin).
29. His _____ hath made herself ready. (Rev. 19:7)
30. Thou shalt _____ them, and the wind shall carry them away. (Isa. 41:16)
31. God planted a garden eastward in _____ . (Gen. 2:8)
32. English letter or double curve.
33. Taken out of the mouth of the lion two legs, or a piece of an _____ . (Amos 3:12)
34. _____ the sickle, for the harvest is ripe. (Joel 3:13, NIV)
35. Silver (abbrev.).
36. She got a papyrus basket for him and coated it with _____ and pitch. (Exod. 2:3, NIV)
37. _____ then that ye walk circumspectly, not as fools, but as wise. (Eph. 5:15)

38. Judge ye not what is _____ ? (Luke 12:57)
40. Greek letter.
41. Stand up: I myself also _____ [2 words] man. (Acts 10:26)
44. German name meaning "Bowman."
45. Ye have an unction from the Holy _____ . (1 John 2:20)
46. Jesus met them, saying, All _____ . (Matt. 28:9)
47. Roman emperor.
48. Begin.
50. Mightily _____ the word of God. (Acts 19:20)
51. The _____ was a cedar in Lebanon. (Ezek. 31:3)

Down

1. Decorated wall section.
2. Where is _____ thy brother? (Gen. 4:9)
3. With their tongues they have _____ deceit. (Rom. 3:13)
4. He that doeth good is of _____ . (3 John 11)
5. Eighth and twelfth letters.
6. _____ , and Meshech, and Tiras. (Gen. 10:2)
7. He went down and dwelt in the top of the rock _____ . (Judg. 15:8)
8. His eyes shall be _____ with wine. (Gen. 49:12)
9. Like a scarecrow in a _____ patch, their idols cannot speak. (Jer. 10:5, NIV)
10. _____ , O thou seer, go, flee thee. (Amos 7:12)
11. Number of fenced cities of Naphtali. (Josh. 20)
12. If a man be found _____ any of his brethren of the children of Israel. (Deut. 24:7)
19. Go quickly.
20. _____ the son of Zephaniah. (Zech. 6:14)
21. And _____ the sacrifices of the dead. (Ps. 106:28)
22. Rachel said, God hath judged me . . . therefore called she his name _____ . (Gen. 30:6)

24. Because of _____ the land mourneth. (Jer. 23:10)
25. False bearer of gifts.
26. _____ ands or maybes.
27. They _____ my path, they set forward my calamity. (Job 30:13)
28. 1001 (rom. num.).
30. The night is _____ spent, the day is at hand. (Rom. 13:12)
31. The poor man had nothing, save one little _____ lamb. (2 Sam. 12:3)
33. To him that overcometh will I give to _____ of the hidden manna. (Rev. 2:17)
34. And there was no more _____. (Rev. 21:1)

36. They shall build, but I will _____ down. (Mal. 1:4)
37. Sources.
39. If an ox _____ a man or a woman. (Exod. 21:28)
40. Cainan, which was the son of _____. (Luke 3:37–38)
41. Dog-faced ape.
42. Mattanaih, the son of _____. (Neh. 11:22, NIV)
43. Danish measure.
45. Edible root.
46. The elder unto the elect lady and _____ children. (2 John 1:1)
49. The time of _____ departure is at hand. (2 Tim. 4:6)

30

Across

1. Who did no sin, neither _____ guile found in his mouth. (1 Peter 2:22)
4. If her father had but _____ in her face. (Num. 12:14)
8. If a man or woman has a sore on the head or on the _____ . (Lev. 13:29, NIV)
12. Soul (French).
13. Wine measure.
14. The labourer is worthy of his _____ . (Luke 10:7)
15. Speak thou the things which become sound _____ . (Titus 2:1)
17. _____ this, I pray thee. (Isa. 29:11)
18. The angels which kept not their first _____ . (Jude 6)
19. May (month; French).
21. Round plate.
23. Seraiah, the son of _____ . (1 Chron. 4:35)
27. Among (abbrev.).
30. Anglo-Saxon letters.
32. I wish I could be with you now and change my _____ . (Gal. 4:20, NIV)
33. Pet name of Dorothy.
35. Hindu sect.
37. As it was in the days of _____ . (Luke 17:26)
38. Be ye _____ of the word. (James 1:22)
40. Let him _____ peace, and ensue it. (1 Peter 3:11)
42. Baseball position (abbrev.).
43. The ark rested . . . upon the mountains of _____ . (Gen. 8:4)
45. Black.
47. _____ firma.
49. A damsel came to hearken, named _____ . (Acts 12:13)
52. Take heed that ye despise not one of these little _____ . (Matt. 18:10)
54. Because of _____ they were broken off, and thou standest by faith. (Rom. 11:20)
56. Ye see a cloud rise out of the _____ . (Luke 12:54)
57. His hairs were white like wool, as white as _____ . (Rev. 1:14)
58. Of serpents, and of things in the _____ , is tamed. (James 3:7)
59. Remember _____ wife. (Luke 17:32)
60. He will surely violently turn and _____ thee like a ball. (Isa. 22:18)
61. They _____ in vision, they stumble in judgment. (Isa. 28:7)

Down

1. Bare your legs, and _____ through the streams. (Isa. 47:2, NIV)
2. _____ , which was the son of Naum. (Luke 3:25)
3. Ringleader of the _____ of the Nazarenes. (Acts 24:5)
4. A sally.
5. O _____ , that despise my name. (Mal. 1:6)
6. There was no room for them in the _____ . (Luke 2:7)
7. The Nile will _____ with frogs. (Exod. 8:3, NIV)
8. As _____ hath suffered for us in the flesh, arm yourselves likewise. (1 Peter 4:1)
9. Hasten.
10. _____ the son of Ikkesh. (1 Chron. 27:9)
11. Man's name.
16. Slight amount.
20. Lava.
22. Greek letters.
24. Electrically charged atom.
25. Seth, to him also there was born a son; and he called his name _____ . (Gen. 4:26)
26. Punish the men that are settled on their _____ . (Zeph. 1:12)
27. Who of you by worrying can _____ [2 words] single hour to his life? (Luke 12:25, NIV)
28. Secure.
29. The _____ of these is charity. (1 Cor. 13:13)
31. Snow runner.
34. Legally detains.
36. Are they _____ ? so am I. (2 Cor. 11:22)
39. Sparoid fish.

41. Eye cosmetic.
44. Again, I will put my _____ in him. (Heb. 2:13)
46. The heavens shall pass away with a great _____ . (2 Peter 3:10)
48. _____ Domini.
50. The hart, and the roebuck, and the fallow _____ . (Deut. 14:5)

51. He that lacketh these things is blind, and cannot see _____ off. (2 Peter 1:9)
52. The _____ also and the raven shall dwell in it. (Isa. 34:11)
53. Recent (prefix).
55. Cattle genus.

31

Across

1. There was one _____ , a prophetess. (Luke 2:36)
5. When they saw the _____ , they rejoiced. (Matt. 2:10)
9. Aaron thy brother died in mount _____ . (Deut. 32:50)
12. Color of a horse.
13. You will be protected from the _____ of the tongue. (Job 5:21, NIV)
14. Fifth son of Bela. (1 Chron. 7:7)
15. Lose.
16. He _____ first to Mary Magdalene. (Mark 16:9)
18. A simple man _____ anything. (Prov. 14:15, NIV)
20. The covert of the reed, and _____ . (Job 40:21)
21. The letter c.
22. The letter f.
23. Like a garment; the _____ will eat them up. (Isa. 50:9, NIV)
26. Behold, all his _____ shall be ashamed. (Isa. 44:11)
31. The sons of Eliphaz; Teman and _____ . (1 Chron. 1:36)
32. Large quantity.
33. Ginko tree.
34. He shall send them a _____ , and a great one. (Isa. 19:20)
36. He said, "Absolute power corrupts absolutely."
37. Quiet digraph.
38. Who _____ thou, O great mountain? (Zech. 4:7)
39. I am not _____ but unto the lost sheep. (Matt. 15:24)
42. For all the _____ of God in him are yea. (2 Cor. 1:20)
47. More worthy of faith.
49. _____ in three years came the navy. (1 Kings 10:22)
50. Go to the _____ , thou sluggard. (Prov. 6:6)
51. They covered him with clothes, but he gat no _____ . (1 Kings 1:1)
52. Write it before them in a table, and _____ it in a book. (Isa. 30:8)

53. _____ , I am coming soon. (Rev. 22:20, NIV).
54. Norse saga.
55. Past tense of "swim" (obs.)

Down

1. _____ , and Dumah, and Eshean. (Josh. 15:52)
2. Alaskan city.
3. Out of him came forth the corner, out of him the _____ . (Zech. 10:4)
4. Even now are there many _____ . (1 John 2:18)
5. Is Israel a servant? is he a homeborn _____ ? (Jer. 2:14)
6. Bind.
7. The gall of _____ within him. (Job 20:14)
8. Unit of fluidity.
9. The ringstraked shall be thy _____ . (Gen. 31:8)
10. Ram the firstborn, and Bunah, and _____ , and Ozem, and Abijah. (1 Chron. 2:25)
11. Relieves.
17. Many are the _____ of the righteous. (Ps. 34:19)
19. Eyes (Scottish).
22. God (Hebrew).
23. Months (abbrev.).
24. Tumor (suffix).
25. Hebrew letter.
26. I pray not _____ the world. (John 17:9)
27. There is a woman that hath a familiar spirit at _____-Dor. (1 Sam. 28:7)
28. October (abbrev.).
29. _____ can open the doors of his face? (Job 41:14)
30. He that hath the _____ hath life. (1 John 5:12)
32. You (Italian).
35. _____ that my head were waters. (Jer. 9:1)
36. I have broken the _____ of Pharaoh. (Ezek. 30:21)
38. Major artery.
39. Make speed, haste, _____ not. (1 Sam. 20:38)

40. Sea falcon.
41. I went down into the garden of ______ to see the fruits. (Song of Sol. 6:11)
42. Blotched.
43. When ye ______, ye may understand. (Eph. 3:4)
44. I wash myself with ______ water. (Job 9:30)
45. Outer (prefix).
46. I may not ______ as if I would terrify you by letters. (2 Cor. 10:9)
48. Which have received ______ Holy Ghost as well as we? (Acts 10:47)

32

Across

1. Plant fiber.
5. I have _____ you with milk. (1 Cor. 3:2)
8. Thou shouldest _____ a fool in a mortar among wheat. (Prov. 27:22)
12. _____ , who for one morsel of meat sold his birthright. (Heb. 12:16)
13. I have made you a tester of metals and my people the _____ . (Jer. 6:27)
14. Annual cereal grass.
15. Sir (German).
16. Vase.
17. Taj Mahal site.
18. Who can forgive _____ but God only? (Mark 2:7)
20. Out of _____ his bread shall be fat. (Gen. 49:20)
21. To make all grace _____ toward you. (2 Cor. 9:8)
24. Ye fast for strife and debate, and to smite with the _____ of wickedness. (Isa. 58:4)
25. Thou hast _____ eyes within thy locks. (Song of Sol. 4:1)
26. How is the gold become _____ ! (Lam. 4:1)
27. _____ , lama sabachthani! (Matt. 27:46)
30. Mamre the Amorite, brother of Eshcol, and brother of _____ . (Gen. 14:13)
31. We _____ our bread with the peril of our lives. (Lam. 5:9)
32. Sewed fig leaves together and made themselves _____ coverings. (Gen. 3:7, ASV)
33. Sea (French).
34. Riblah, on the east side of _____ . (Num. 34:11)
35. He _____ no place of repentance, though he sought it. (Heb. 12:17)
36. _____ shall make the young men cheerful. (Zech. 9:17)
38. Their _____ are also swifter than the leopards. (Hab. 1:8)
39. As for the _____ , the fir trees are her house. (Ps. 104:17)
41. Flee as a _____ to your mountain. (Ps. 11:1)

42. Quails came up, and covered the _____ . (Exod. 16:13)
43. They have no rest day _____ night. (Rev. 14:11)
44. Shimei the son of _____ . (2 Sam. 19:16)
48. Killed some twenty men in an _____ of about half an acre. (1 Sam. 14:14, NIV)
49. Wrath.
50. Thou shalt make them as a fiery _____ . (Ps. 21:9)
51. Hebrew letter.
52. The _____ of all things is at hand. (1 Peter 4:7)
53. I forgave thee all that _____ . (Matt. 18:32)

Down

1. Expression of surprise.
2. Direction from Jerusalem to Bethlehem.
3. They _____ my path. (Job 30:13)
4. They are gone without strength before the _____ . (Lam. 1:6)
5. Neither was guile _____ in his mouth. (1 Peter 2:22)
6. He who makes haste with his feet _____ . (Prov. 19:2, ASV)
7. Make the cities of Judah desolate, and a _____ of dragons. (Jer. 10:22)
8. I am become as sounding _____ . (1 Cor. 13:1)
9. I came not to call the _____ , but sinners. (Mark 2:17)
10. An half _____ of land, which a yoke of oxen might plow. (1 Sam. 14:14)
11. Lord, let it alone this _____ also. (Luke 13:8)
19. Opposite of outs.
20. Her _____ is to be devoted to the Lord. (1 Cor. 7:34, NIV)
21. For _____ was first formed. (1 Tim. 2:13)
22. A _____ of him shall not be broken. (John 19:36)
23. He who _____ will inherit all this. (Rev. 21:7, NIV)

A crossword grid with numbered cells: 1, 2, 3, 4, 5, 6, 7, 8, 9, 10, 11 (top row); 12, 13, 14; 15, 16, 17; 18, 19, 20; 21, 22, 23, 24; 25, 26, 27, 28, 29; 30, 31, 32; 33, 34, 35; 36, 37, 38; 39, 40, 41; 42, 43, 44, 45, 46, 47; 48, 49, 50; 51, 52, 53.

24. Is it _____ to say to a king, Thou art wicked? (Job 34:18)

26. _____ shall be a serpent by the way. (Gen. 49:17)

28. Judgment also will I lay to the _____ . (Isa. 28:17)

29. Indians (poetic).

31. The _____ shall take him by the heel. (Job 18:9)

32. The _____ [2 words] giveth them light. (Rev. 22:5)

34. Make thee an _____ of gopher wood. (Gen. 6:14)

35. _____ the ear trieth words, as the mouth tasteth meat. (Job 34:3)

37. _____ kissed her mother-in-law. (Ruth 1:14)

38. Because no man hath _____ us. (Matt. 20:7)

39. The priest shall pronounce him clean; it is only a _____ from the burn. (Lev. 13:28, NIV)

40. Two she bears out of the wood, and _____ forty and two children. (2 Kings 2:24)

41. Whosoever is _____ of God sinneth not. (1 John 5:18)

43. Never (German).

45. The serpent beguiled _____ . (2 Cor. 11:3)

46. Hebrew teacher.

47. Go to the _____ , thou sluggard. (Prov. 6:6)

33

Across

1. The days of _____ were nine hundred and five years. (Gen. 5:11)
5. Species of woody vine.
8. _____ opened the book in the sight of all the people. (Neh. 8:5)
12. But other of the apostles saw I _____ . (Gal. 1:19)
13. Small toy dog (diminutive).
14. Yet will they _____ upon the LORD. (Mic. 3:11)
15. The roebuck, and the fallow _____ . (Deut. 14:5)
16. At _____ , we were bold in our God to speak. (1 Thess. 2:2)
18. Calf meat.
20. I have eaten _____ like bread. (Ps. 102:9)
21. Anoint _____ to be king over Syria. (1 Kings 19:15)
24. _____ of glass mingled with fire. (Rev. 15:2)
25. Sorcery, interprets _____ , engages in witchcraft. (Deut. 18:10, NIV)
26. Who _____ thou that judgest another? (James 4:12)
27. Receive him _____ into your house, neither bid him God speed. (2 John 10)
30. You made a _____ with those whose beds you love. (Isa. 57:8, NIV)
31. Then _____ was wroth with the seer. (2 Chron. 16:10)
32. A _____ vision has been shown to me. (Isa. 21:2, NIV)
33. Anglo-Saxon letter.
34. Shall make an _____ of shittim wood. (Exod. 25:10)
35. If a blind man _____ a blind man. (Matt. 15:14)
36. Smallest, indivisible particle.
38. His servant _____ , the son of Nun. (Exod. 33:11)
39. O house of _____ , trust in the LORD. (Ps. 115:10)
41. The _____ that is in thy brother's eye. (Luke 6:42)
42. _____ our dearly beloved, and fellow-labourer. (Philem. 1)
44. Whither have ye made a _____ to day? (1 Sam. 27:10)
48. Shut up the words, and _____ the book. (Dan. 12:4)
49. Men from Babylon, and from Cuthah, and from _____ . (2 Kings 17:24)
50. In the process of _____ it came to pass. (Gen. 4:3)
51. Anglo-Saxon letters.
52. Alkaline.
53. For sin . . . deceived me, and by it _____ me. (Rom. 7:11)

Down

1. The _____ of all flesh is come before me. (Gen. 6:13)
2. Until the day that _____ entered into the ark. (Luke 17:27)
3. Beloved, let us love _____ another. (1 John 4:7)
4. Thou art no more a _____ . (Gal. 4:7)
5. To grow faint (obs.).
6. Eye cosmetic.
7. Zebaim, the children of _____ . (Ezra 2:57)
8. French form from "Elizabeth."
9. Hen, the son of _____ . (Zech. 6:14)
10. Oily seed.
11. Philippine fennel.
17. Little children, it is the _____ time. (2 Peter 3:3)
19. Eyes (Scottish).
21. Looking for that blessed _____ . (Titus 2:13)
22. Alammelech, and _____ , and Misheal. (Josh. 19:26)
23. Iddo the son of _____ . (1 Chron. 27:21)
24. Sons of Jether; Jephunnah, and Pispah, and _____ . (1 Chron. 7:38)
26. If any of you lack wisdom, let him _____ of God. (James 1:5)
28. Turkish troops.
29. Indian buzzard.
31. I have broken the _____ of Pharaoh. (Ezek. 30:21)
32. They wandered in _____ , and in mountains. (Heb. 11:38)

34. Top quality (2 words).
35. Just _____, vexed with the filthy conversation. (2 Peter 2:7)
37. Fixed fees.
38. He spake by the hand of his servant _____, the son of Amittai. (2 Kings 14:25)
39. Bishop's seat.
40. Egyptian month.

41. Shall not a dog _____ his tongue. (Exod. 11:7)
43. They _____ my path, they set forward my calamity. (Job 30:13)
45. My head with _____ thou didst not anoint. (Luke 7:46)
46. Soul (French).
47. God give thee the _____ of heaven. (Gen. 27:28)

34

Across

1. _____ him take the water of life freely. (Rev. 22:17)
4. Zhivago's love.
8. Is anything too _____ for the LORD? (Gen. 18:14)
12. Gold (Spanish).
13. A prophet of the LORD was there, whose name was _____. (2 Chron. 28:9)
14. If he is in the _____, I will track him down. (1 Sam. 23:23, NIV)
15. Ye, being rooted and _____ in love. (Eph. 3:17)
17. Let us draw _____ with a true heart. (Heb. 10:22)
18. Woman's nickname.
19. How right they are to _____ you. (Song of Sol. 1:4, NIV)
20. The conies are but a _____ folk. (Prov. 30:26)
23. Tuesday's namesake.
24. Strangely.
25. I could not _____ you as spiritual but as worldly. (1 Cor. 3:1, NIV)
29. Hemp plant.
30. Science of (suffix).
31. Their _____ of pleasure is to carouse. (2 Peter 2:13, NIV)
32. When I had eaten it, my _____ turned sour. (Rev. 10:10, NIV)
34. Let him that stole _____ no more. (Eph. 4:28)
35. Direction from Jerusalem to Jericho.
36. If any man _____, let him come unto me. (John 7:37)
37. In the sweat of thy face shalt thou eat _____. (Gen. 3:19)
40. The glory of Jacob shall be made _____. (Isa. 17:4)
41. These shall make war with the _____. (Rev. 17:14)
42. The grace of God that _____ salvation. (Titus 2:11)
46. Thou canst not bear them which are _____. (Rev. 2:2)
47. Senior (French).
48. The letter v.
49. Past tense of "are."
50. Have they not _____? Have they not divided the prey? (Judg. 5:30)
51. O heavens, and give _____, O earth. (Isa. 1:2)

Down

1. The priest shall take some of the _____ of oil, and pour it. (Lev. 14:15)
2. It is a people that do _____ in their heart. (Ps. 95:10)
3. Also.
4. Jesus often withdrew to _____ places. (Luke 5:16, NIV)
5. Confuse.
6. The earth shall _____ to and fro like a drunkard. (Isa. 24:20)
7. The LORD shall _____ to me another son. (Gen. 30:24)
8. Blotting out the _____ of ordinances that was against us. (Col. 2:14)
9. Air (comb. form).
10. Wilt thou _____ it up in three days? (John 2:20)
11. For we _____ not make ourselves of the number. (2 Cor. 10:12)
16. Present you holy and _____. (Col. 1:22)
19. I am troubled; O Lord, come to my _____. (Isa. 38:14, NIV)
20. Castle moat.
21. Revise for publication.
22. Taro roots.
23. Football scores (abbrev.).
25. Alas (German).

26. Mahli, and _____ , and Jerimoth. (1 Chron. 23:23)
27. Oceans.
28. Ye are the _____ of the earth. (Matt. 5:13)
30. He casteth forth his _____ like morsels. (Ps. 147:17)
33. _____ filleth the hungry soul with goodness. (Ps. 107:9)
34. Out of Zion, the perfection of beauty, God hath _____ . (Ps. 50:2)
36. For _____ is the kingdom. (Matt. 6:13)
37. When the south wind _____ softly. (Acts 27:13)
38. Speak irrationally.
39. Moslem ruler.
40. Who have purposed to _____ up my feet. (Ps. 140:4, ASV)
42. _____ relief.
43. Adam knew _____ his wife. (Gen. 4:1)
44. Beverage.
45. Jesus saith unto _____ , Give me to drink. (John 4:7)

35

Across

1. He will surely violently turn and
   _____ thee like a ball. (Isa. 22:18)
5. They have gone in the way of _____.
   (Jude 11)
9. I _____ a queen, and am no widow.
   (Rev. 18:7)
12. I gave unto Isaac Jacob and _____.
    (Josh. 24:4)
13. An half _____ of land, which a yoke
    of oxen might plow. (1 Sam. 14:14)
14. _____ of men sought we glory.
    (1 Thess. 2:6)
15. The _____, which is the Holy Ghost.
    (John 14:26)
17. The children of Lod, Hadid, and
    _____. (Ezra 2:33)
18. The _____ shall overflow with wine.
    (Joel 2:24)
19. I will pay that that I have _____.
    (Jonah 2:9)
21. Then shall ye give me thirty _____.
    (Judg. 14:13)
24. Will a young lion cry out of his
    _____. (Amos 3:4)
25. Mine eye poureth out _____ unto
    God. (Job 16:20)
26. I have a _____ from God unto thee.
    (Judg. 3:20)
30. All that handle the _____. (Ezek.
    27:29)
31. Snake-like fish.
32. Why then doth their king inherit
    _____. (Jer. 49:1)
33. The Lord was _____ to heal them.
    (Luke 5:17)
36. How right they are to _____ you!
    (Song of Sol. 1:4, NIV)
38. Old times (archaic).
39. _____, the son of Gideoni. (Num.
    1:11)
40. _____ said, Turn again, my
    daughters. (Ruth 1:8)
43. Last word of the New Testament.
44. I am too _____ to have an husband.
    (Ruth 1:12)
45. The city of my God, which is new
    _____. (Rev. 3:12)
50. Japanese national park.

51. _____! for that day is great. (Jer.
    30:7)
52. Past tense of "heave."
53. From mount _____ ye shall point out
    your border. (Num. 34:8)
54. The garden of God could not _____
    him. (Ezek. 31:8)
55. Let me have some of that red _____!
    (Gen. 25:30, NIV)

Down

1. Detective.
2. Bear (Spanish).
3. Diminutive for "Samuel."
4. Thou shalt not _____ a witch to live.
   (Exod. 22:18)
5. Joseph gave them _____, as
   Pharaoh had commanded. (Gen.
   45:21, NIV)
6. Men shall speak of the might of thy
   terrible _____. (Ps. 145:6)
7. Wrath.
8. Courage.
9. She is not afraid of the _____. (Prov.
   31:21)
10. Scottish island.
11. The old path that evil men have
    _____. (Job 22:15, NIV)
16. Breakfast cereal.
20. Opposite of offs.
21. Get thee down, that the rain _____
    thee not. (1 Kings 18:44)
22. How shall they _____ without a
    preacher? (Rom. 10:14)
23. Ear (Old English).
24. Of the (Spanish).
26. Mercy and truth are _____ together.
    (Ps. 85:10)
27. Who is _____ [2 words] like unto
    thee? (Mic. 7:18)
28. African tie-dyed cloth.
29. Thou hast been in _____ the garden
    of God. (Ezek. 28:13)
31. Her _____ is as bitter as wormwood.
    (Prov. 5:4)
34. Arphaxad, which was the son of
    _____. (Luke 3:36)
35. _____ the Tishbite. (1 Kings 17:1)
36. Lincoln and Vigota.

1 2 3 4 5 6 7 8 9 10 11
12 13 14
15 16 17
18 19 20
21 22 23 24
25 26 27 28 29
30 31 32
33 34 35 36 37
38 39
40 41 42 43
44 45 46 47 48 49
50 51 52
53 54 55

37. Simeon and Levi, ______ brethren. (Gen. 34:25)
39. Call for Samson, that he may ______ us. (Judg. 16:25, ASV)
40. By faith ______, being warned of God of things not seen as yet. (Heb. 11:7)
41. Christ ______ suffered for us. (1 Peter 2:21)
42. There is a bad ______, for he has been there four days. (John 11:39, NIV)
43. King ______ the Canaanite. (Num. 21:1)
46. The two sons of ______, Hophni and Phinehas. (1 Sam. 1:3)
47. Haran begat ______. (Gen. 11:27)
48. The serpent beguiled ______. (2 Cor. 11:3)
49. Cat cry.

1

A	S	S			S	O	N	G			W	H	A	T
R	A	N			S	T	O	A			E	A	S	E
A	R	A			S	I	A	L			E	V	I	L
M	A	G	I		C	H	I	C	K	E	N	S		
			S	H				L	A	S				
N	A	T	H	A	N	A	E	L			D	A	Y	
U	S	E			R	A	H	A	M			O	D	E
N	A	N			B	O	A	N	E	R	G	E	S	
			T	O	M			D	O					
I	S	C	A	R	I	O	T			E	D	E	N	
S	P	A	N			A	D	A	M			E	D	O
L	E	V	I			N	O	M	E			A	N	O
E	W	E	S			D	R	E	W			D	A	N

4

H	A	T			A	G	A	R			S	H	O	D
A	S	H			S	H	U	T			H	O	M	E
S	S	I			L	O	N	E			I	R	R	A
T	E	M	P	E	S	T			S	P	A	I	N	
				R	E	T			S	E	M			
S	L	O	O	P			P	L	E	A	S	E	D	
E	P	I	C			W	A	Y			S	A	L	E
B	I	L	L	O	W	S			S	T	Y	L	E	
			A	L	I			W	O	E				
D	A	V	I	D			J	O	U	R	N	E	Y	
A	D	A	M			N	O	U	N			E	V	E
Y	A	L	E			E	I	L	D			B	E	D
S	H	E	D			E	N	D	S			O	N	O

2

A	H	A	B			G	N	U			H	E	R	A
D	A	D	E			I	O	N			A	M	O	S
A	L	I	T			N	E	H	E	M	I	A	H	
M	O	T	H	S			L	A	D			T	R	Y
			L	I	T			T	A	J				
G	E	N	E	S	I	S			M	E	R	A	B	
A	D	A	H			P	O	I			R	U	L	E
W	O	M	E	N			S	A	M	U	E	L	S	
			M	A	N			M	O	S				
S	A	Y			M	O	A			B	A	B	E	L
P	R	O	V	E	R	B	S			L	O	V	E	
A	B	L	E			T	I	E			E	L	I	A
T	A	K	E			H	A	T			M	E	L	D

5

A	R	A	B			S	A	U	L			S	A	P
S	A	R	I			I	L	S	E			A	M	I
K	I	N	G	O	F	B	A	B	Y	L	O	N		
			V	A	T			A	E	O	N	S		
S	P	E	A	K			B	A	N	A	L			
L	E	V	I			J	U	D	A	H			F	E
E	R	E			S	A	R	A	H			B	O	Z
W	E			C	H	I	R	M			A	S	E	R
			H	E	A	L	S			A	M	A	S	A
I	C	O	N	S				A	D	A				
S	H	E	T	H	A	R	B	O	Z	N	A	I		
L	A	R			A	H	A	B			E	A	R	N
E	R	S			I	O	N	A			D	E	A	N

3

L	O	V	E			A	S	S	T			R	A	N
E	V	I	L			G	A	L	A			E	V	E
R	E	N	D			A	W	E	N			M	E	T
P	R	E	E	M	I	N	E	N	C	E				
			R	O	N			P	E	R	M	I	T	
L	E	O			A	S	S			R	A	B	B	I
A	L	V	A			T	A	W			B	E	L	L
S	M	E	L	T			A	I	L			R	E	L
H	O	R	S	E	S			T	E	A				
			C	O	M	M	A	N	D	M	E	N	T	
O	N	O			P	E	R	E			E	L	I	A
I	A	M			L	A	I	S			N	U	L	L
L	Y	E			E	R	A	S			S	L	E	E

6

G	N	A	T			A	S	H			T	A	H	A
U	N	T	O			N	E	E			E	B	E	N
T	E	E	N			T	E	A	C	H	E	R	S	
				G	E	S			L	U	E	L	L	A
A	R	G	U	E			F	I	R	E				
N	I	N	E			M	I	N	I	S	T	E	R	
E	M	U			L	I	E	G	E			R	A	E
W	E	S	T	E	R	N	S			M	E	S	A	
			E	G	A	D			P	E	T	E	R	
M	O	S	A	I	C			A	I	M				
A	P	O	S	T	L	E	S			B	O	D	E	
T	A	M	E			E	R	A			E	D	E	N
S	H	E	D			S	S	S			R	E	N	D

7

```
F I T S   L E A F   C R Y
A S I A   E V I E   O Y E
T H E R E V E L A T I O N
    D E I     R E N T S
P U P I L   W A N E S
O N E S   B O L O S   D O
S T A   E R U P T   A R K
T O   S P I N S   S T A R
    E P H O D   O M E G A
R A N E E     A C Y
O F J E S U S C H R I S T
M A O   U N I T   N A T E
P R Y   S O N S   A M E N
```

10

```
A S S E   G A D   M A R C
L O L L   A L L   E L I A
P H I L I P P I   S E A L
S O M I T   H I M S E L F
    S E T   I R I
S A T   M E N   S A R A H
E M I T   A I M   H O R A
M I C A H   T A R   T E M
    U A J   D O G
C O U N T E D   O L I V E
A G N I   S U F F E R E D
E L I S   U S E   A R I D
N E T H   S T Y   M A N Y
```

8

```
M O D E   M A P   S A N E
A M E N   O L L   A G O N
D A U G H T E R   L O R D
E N T   I T E   H E
    E G O   L A M E N T
B O O T H   D I M   P E E
A B B A   A R E   S H A N
D O E   F E Y   H E A R D
E L D E R S   W A R
    B Y   H O T   S P A
A N N O   J E R E M I A H
N O O N   O L D   A R I A
D O T Y   B L S   H E R B
```

11

```
F A T S   A S E R   P R O
A D I A   N A M E   R E G
C O M M A N D E D   E A R
S W E L T E R   A C R E
    A E X   L A K E
R E S H   E S C A P E D
A N T   D A N T E   T A U
Y E A R N E D   E S T E
    T E A R   A R N
S O U L   E N E M I E S
A C T   J U D G M E N T S
U T E   O S E E   S E N T
I O S   B E L L   H E A S
```

9

```
D A Y S   A L S   F A C S
E L E C   M A H   I L A I
A F A R   O R A   R A I N
D A R I U S   D Y E I N G
    B S   S R O
A I D E   C H A L D E A N
S T A   S H O C K   A G O
H A N A N I A H   F R E T
    E L L   H I
R A I N E D   D A N I E L
A N G E   R O E   G O R E
H O A X   E N E   E N S E
S A L I   N O D   R A C E
```

12

```
B E E F   A T O P   R E B
E D A R   M A G I   E R E
A E R I   P L E A S U R E
U N N E T   L E N T
    N E E   S O R R O W
C O N D E M N   S A I T H
A R O O   S A T   I N T O
S T U F F   K I N G D O M
T O N G U E   P O H
    O L L A   S T A L E
B R I D L E T H   W R E N
O A R   E N O S   A M O K
A M A   R A M S   Y E N I
```

13

D	R	E	W		S	E	M		S	A	L	S
O	A	T	H		E	V	A		E	D	I	T
E	S	T	E		E	E	N		E	A	S	E
S	H	A	L	L	K	N	O	W	T	H	A	T
			P	O	H		R	E	H			
A	B	A		O	I	L			A	R	T	E
I	A	M	I	N	M	Y	F	A	T	H	E	R
M	A	I	N			E	A	T		O	A	R
			F	R	A		M	R	S			
I	N	M	E	A	N	D	I	I	N	Y	O	U
D	A	I	S		N	O	N		A	E	O	N
L	I	N	T		O	N	E		R	A	N	I
E	L	T	S		Y	E	S		E	R	A	T

16

C	R	O	P		W	O	E		J	O	E	L
H	A	G	I		R	A	N		E	S	A	U
E	S	E	L		O	R	E		T	E	R	M
T	H	E	A	C	T	S		S	H	E	E	P
			T	E	E		O	U	R			
J	A	M	E	S		T	I	M	O	T	H	Y
A	R	E			S	O	L			R	U	E
M	A	T	T	H	E	W		R	E	I	G	N
			H	A	M		E	E	L			
W	A	G	E	S		E	P	H	E	S	U	S
O	M	R	I		A	S	H		V	A	N	E
R	O	A	R		S	E	A		E	N	T	E
D	I	M	S		I	S	H		N	E	O	N

14

A	K	A	N		H	A	M		C	A	L	F
D	E	M	O		A	G	O		O	R	A	L
A	P	O	S	T	L	E	S		M	A	R	A
M	I	S	E	R		S	E	A	M			
			D	O	R		S	C	A	R	E	D
E	T	O		D	A	N		E	N	E	M	Y
A	R	M	S		G	A	D		D	I	M	E
T	I	R	E	D		G	O	D		S	A	D
S	P	I	R	I	T		W	I	T			
			V	E	I	L		S	A	U	C	Y
D	A	T	A		D	I	S	C	I	P	L	E
E	V	E	N		A	M	I		N	O	O	N
W	A	N	T		L	E	T		T	N	T	S

17

F	R	A	S		R	A	N	K		A	P	T
R	I	C	H		A	L	I	I		C	A	R
E	P	H	E	S	I	A	N	S		T	R	E
T	E	E		A	N	Y		S	W	A	R	E
			S	K	Y		D	E	I			
S	M	I	L	E		M	E	S	S	I	A	H
T	A	R	A		I	R	E		D	A	R	E
P	R	A	Y	E	R	S		S	O	N	A	R
			E	L	I		T	O	M			
T	E	R	R	I		U	R	N		S	T	A
A	T	E		J	E	R	U	S	A	L	E	M
R	O	E		A	L	A	S		S	I	L	O
E	N	D		H	A	L	T		A	M	E	N

15

E	R	R		T	A	L	C		A	D	A	M
P	E	E		O	D	O	R		C	A	G	E
I	S	A		A	I	D	E		T	R	O	T
C	H	R	I	S	T	I	A	N	S			
			S	T	S		T	O		A	B	I
I	D	O	L	S		F	O	R		B	E	L
R	A	S	E		C	O	R		A	B	E	L
A	T	E		T	O	E		B	R	A	S	S
D	E	E		O	M		M	O	A			
			C	O	M	M	I	T	M	E	N	T
I	D	E	A		A	U	N	T		V	I	E
L	E	V	I		N	I	N	O		I	N	N
L	I	E	N		D	R	A	M		L	E	T

18

A	N	T		M	I	S	T		F	E	E	D
L	O	O		A	N	N	O		O	N	D	E
I	A	M		K	N	O	W	L	E	D	G	E
T	H	E	R	E		W	E	A		S	E	R
			E	T	E		R	I	B			
F	U	R	T	H	E	R		R	A	B	B	I
E	S	A	U		L	A	R		T	E	E	S
W	E	I	R	D		R	E	S	T	E	T	H
			N	A	P		O	I	L			
A	G	A		N	U	L		N	E	C	K	S
W	A	N	D	E	R	I	N	G		H	E	M
A	L	E	E		S	O	U	L		U	N	U
Y	A	R	N		E	N	T	E		N	O	T

19

C	O	O	L		H	A	R	P		A	L	L
A	E	R	I		I	C	E	R		L	E	A
B	R	O	K	E	N	H	E	A	R	T	E	D
			E	N	D			Y	E	A	R	S
S	M	O	T	E		S	W	E	A	R		
L	E	A	H		H	E	A	R	D		U	P
E	R	R		B	E	A	R	S		S	P	A
W	E		U	R	A	L	S		M	A	G	I
		S	L	E	D	S		V	I	G	O	R
A	R	E	N	A			A	I	R			
J	U	D	A	S	I	S	C	A	R	I	O	T
A	S	A		T	R	O	T		O	R	N	E
R	A	N		S	I	N	S		R	A	I	N

22

L	O	B	E		A	R	E	A		I	L	L
A	S	E	A		D	E	A	N		D	E	I
M	A	G	S		D	A	R	K	N	E	S	S
B	R	O	T	H	E	R		L	E	A	S	T
		T	E	E	D		L	E	T			
P	E	T	R	A		B	E	S		B	S	S
O	X	E	N		S	A	D		S	L	O	E
T	E	N		F	A	T		S	T	E	R	N
			S	I	T		C	U	R	S	E	D
A	N	G	E	L		E	L	I	A	S		
S	O	M	E	T	I	M	E		N	I	S	I
E	V	E		H	A	I	R		G	N	A	T
R	A	N		Y	O	L	K		E	G	G	S

20

A	R	A	S		G	A	P		Z	A	R	A
M	U	C	H		A	B	A		E	D	E	N
I	D	D	O		R	U	N		L	I	S	A
S	E	C	O	N	D	T	I	M	O	T	H	Y
			T	O	E		C	U	T			
H	E	N		E	N	S		D	E	A	L	T
A	M	O	S		S	A	T		S	T	A	R
D	E	V	I	L		W	I	T		E	R	Y
			N	E	O		M	A	N			
S	O	N	G	O	F	S	O	L	O	M	O	N
I	L	A	I		F	I	T		R	A	G	E
R	E	I	N		E	D	H		T	R	E	E
S	O	N	G		R	E	Y		H	E	E	D

23

G	A	R	B		B	E	D		C	A	S	T
I	D	A	E		A	R	E		I	D	E	A
L	E	S	S		D	E	C		M	E	E	T
A	W	H	I	L	E		L	A	B	O	R	S
			D	O		P	A	I	R			
T	A	R	E		M	A	R	R	I	A	G	E
I	R	A		W	I	N	E	S		R	I	N
C	O	M	F	O	R	T	S		M	I	N	D
			E	R	A	S		H	O			
F	E	N	N	E	C		A	A	R	O	N	S
A	L	E	C		L	O	T		R	A	I	L
L	I	M	E		E	R	R		O	T	T	O
A	S	A	D		S	E	E		W	H	E	T

21

A	S	P	S		A	S	S		B	A	L	E
R	O	U	T		D	E	N		U	C	A	L
A	E	R	O		D	N	A		R	A	C	A
			P	R	Y		T	R	O	D	D	E	N
B	R	O	K	E	N		E	N	E			
A	H	S		T	O	P		A	N	G	E	L
S	E	E	P		D	I	E		S	E	R	E
S	O	D	O	M		E	M	U		N	N	E
			R	E	D		S	M	I	T	E	S
D	E	S	T	R	O	Y		A	M	I		
U	L	A	I		V	O	W		A	L	A	T
N	A	T	O		E	K	E		G	E	B	A
G	M	E	N		S	E	T		E	S	A	U

24

R	E	B	S		G	O	A	T		W	H	O
A	R	A	M		L	A	S	H		H	I	D
P	R	A	I	S	E	T	H	E	L	O	R	D
			T	E	A	S		N	O	S	E	S
M	O	L	T	E	N		O	C	T	O		
O	B	O	E	S		O	W	E		E	M	E
T	E	R	N		A	I	L		E	V	A	N
O	D	D		L	I	L		S	T	E	R	N
			M	A	I	D		F	I	E	R	C	E
A	R	Y	A	N		D	O	R	R			
R	I	G	H	T	E	O	U	S	N	E	S	S
E	G	O		E	V	E	R		A	L	A	S
S	A	D		L	E	S	S		L	I	N	T

25

```
D N A   T A R E   A B E L
R O B   E R I N   C L I O
A A L   M I N I S T E R S
W H E L P   N O I S E S
      A L E F   N O S
S H O V E L E D   N I N E
O U F   S I L A S   N O R
S E C T   S T R A N G E R
    L U I   S E T A
A C O R N S     I P O U R
D R U N K A R D S   A L E
D U D E   L E A F   T A N
U S S R   T O N Y   S I T
```

28

```
L O I   L E A H   T H A T
E N D   A L B A   R U T H
A C E   M O O R   A G E E
P E A C E   W E E D
      O N E   S P I G O T
G R U N T E D   E T U D E
R O L F   L E G   I R O N
A M A I N   L A B O U R S
M A I D E N   D E N
      E B E D   A S H E R
A R A N   S E E R   O N O
D I S C   T E N D   R O C
A P S E   S P E S   A S K
```

26

```
S O N G   S A P   A J A H
A D A R   A B A   F E T E
D A M A S C U S   F R O E
E L E C T   T H E L O R D
      E A T   A R I B
T E A   R A N   E C O L E
A S S I   R A M   T A L L
J E S S E   Y E S   M E L
    E R A S   N O E
S A M A R I A   U N C L E
A B B E   A S H K E L O N
B E L L   L E E   M I N D
A L Y S   O R R   Y O K E
```

29

```
D A U G H T E R   M A N S
A B S O L U T E   E M I T
D E E D   B A D   L O N E
O L D   H A M   H O S E A
      A I L   D E N   T L
S M I T E   M A N   D E I
W I F E   F A N   E D E N
E S S   E A R   S W I N G
A G   T A R   S E E
R I G H T   E T A   A M A
I V O R   O N E   H A I L
N E R O   C O M M E N C E
G R E W   A S S Y R I A N
```

27

```
T H R E A T   T R A C E S
R U L E T H   H A V A N A
E M   N O R   E V E   A V
M B A   M E A D E   A B I
O L G A   E N E   O S L O
R E E L S   T E A C H E R
      A T R I P L E
A J U D A E O   L A B A N
S E N D   S C H   N I N A
I R I   E P H O D   D S M
D O   A P E   P A W   W E
E M E T I C   E R A S E R
S E L E C T   D E C O R S
```

30

```
W A S   S P I T   C H I N
A M E   O R N E   H I R E
D O C T R I N E   R E A D
E S T A T E   M A I
      D I S C   A S I E L
A M G   E T H S   T O N E
D O R A   S I K H   N O E
D O E R S   S E E K   S S
A R A R A T   E B O N
      T E R R A   R H O D A
O N E S   U N B E L I E F
W E S T   S N O W   S E A
L O T S   T O S S   E R R
```

31

A	N	N	A		S	T	A	R		H	O	R
R	O	A	N		L	A	S	H		I	R	I
A	M	I	T		A	P	P	E	A	R	E	D
B	E	L	I	E	V	E	S		F	E	N	S
		C	E	E			E	F				
M	O	T	H	S		F	E	L	L	O	W	S
O	M	A	R		T	O	N		I	C	H	O
S	A	V	I	O	U	R		A	C	T	O	N
		S	H			A	R	T				
S	E	N	T		P	R	O	M	I	S	E	S
T	R	U	S	T	I	E	R		O	N	C	E
A	N	T		H	E	A	T		N	O	T	E
Y	E	S		E	D	D	A		S	W	O	M

32

H	E	M	P		F	E	D		B	R	A	Y
E	S	A	U		O	R	E		R	I	C	E
H	E	R	R		U	R	N		A	G	R	A
		S	I	N	S		A	S	H	E	R	
A	B	O	U	N	D		F	I	S	T		
D	O	V	E	S		D	I	M		E	L	I
A	N	E	R		G	A	T		L	O	I	N
M	E	R		A	I	N		F	O	U	N	D
		C	O	R	N		H	O	R	S	E	S
S	T	O	R	K		B	I	R	D			
C	A	M	P		N	O	R		G	E	R	A
A	R	E	A		I	R	E		O	V	E	N
R	E	S	H		E	N	D		D	E	B	T

33

E	N	O	S		A	K	A		E	Z	R	A
N	O	N	E		P	O	M		L	E	A	N
D	E	E	R		P	H	I	L	I	P	P	I
		V	E	A	L		A	S	H	E	S	
H	A	Z	A	E	L		A	S	E	A		
O	M	E	N	S		A	R	T		N	O	T
P	A	C	T		A	S	A		D	I	R	E
E	D	H		A	R	K		L	E	A	D	S
		A	T	O	M		J	O	S	H	U	A
A	A	R	O	N		M	O	T	E			
P	H	I	L	E	M	O	N		R	O	A	D
S	E	A	L		A	V	A		T	I	M	E
E	T	H	S		R	E	H		S	L	E	W

34

L	E	T		L	A	R	A		H	A	R	D
O	R	O		O	D	E	D		A	R	E	A
G	R	O	U	N	D	E	D		N	E	A	R
			N	E	L	L		A	D	O	R	E
F	E	E	B	L	E		T	I	W			
O	D	D	L	Y		A	D	D	R	E	S	S
S	I	D	A		I	C	S		I	D	E	A
S	T	O	M	A	C	H		S	T	E	A	L
			E	N	E		T	H	I	R	S	T
B	R	E	A	D		T	H	I	N			
L	A	M	B		B	R	I	N	G	E	T	H
E	V	I	L		A	I	N	E		V	E	E
W	E	R	E		S	P	E	D		E	A	R

35

T	O	S	S		C	A	I	N		S	I	T
E	S	A	U		A	C	R	E		N	O	R
C	O	M	F	O	R	T	E	R		O	N	O
			F	A	T	S		V	O	W	E	D
S	H	E	E	T	S		D	E	N			
T	E	A	R	S		M	E	S	S	A	G	E
O	A	R		E	E	L		G	A	D		
P	R	E	S	E	N	T		A	D	O	R	E
			E	L	D		A	B	I	D	A	N
N	A	O	M	I		A	M	E	N			
O	L	D		J	E	R	U	S	A	L	E	M
A	S	O		A	L	A	S		H	O	V	E
H	O	R		H	I	D	E		S	T	E	W